CHEMISTRY PROBLEMS
AND HOW TO SOLVE THEM

The Author

Paul R. Frey received his doctor's degree in physical chemistry from Oregon State College in 1936. Since that time he has been associated with the chemistry department at Colorado Agricultural and Mechanical College. Dr. Frey also has held teaching positions at York College, Colorado University, and Oregon State College.

The author has written numerous articles based upon original research, principally in the fields of dipole moment values of organic compounds and the utilization of carotene in the animal body. His articles have been published in the *Journal of the American Chemical Society, American Journal of Physiology, Journal of Nutrition, Science, Journal of the American Veterinary Medical Association,* and the *Journal of the Colorado-Wyoming Academy of Science.* Professor Frey is the author of a standard textbook, *College Chemistry.* In addition, he is a member of the American Chemical Society, the Society for Experimental Biology and Medicine, the American Association for the Advancement of Science, the Colorado-Wyoming Academy of Science, Sigma Xi, Phi Kappa Phi, Phi Lambda Upsilon, and Sigma Pi Sigma.

College Outline Series

CHEMISTRY
PROBLEMS

AND
HOW TO
SOLVE THEM

PAUL R. FREY

Barnes & Noble, Inc. New York
Publishers · Booksellers · Since 1874

©

Fourth Edition, 1953

Copyright, 1938, 1940, 1944, 1953
By BARNES & NOBLE, INC.

L. C. catalogue card number: 55–11935

Thirteenth printing, 1956

Formerly published under the title
Mathematics for General Chemistry

PRINTED IN THE UNITED STATES OF AMERICA

Preface

This book was written as an aid to the student in outlining a logical method of attack in the solution of problems in general chemistry. The thorough understanding of a few elementary principles of mathematics and their use in the solution of chemical problems will help eliminate the all too common practice of solving problems according to prescribed formulas. The working of a problem by routine procedure is usually indicative of a lack of understanding of the concepts involved and their relationship one to the other. The solved problems in the book stress the chemical, physical, and mathematical concepts involved. Consistent use is made of dimensions and the rules applying to significant digits. Such usage tends to promote deductive reasoning on the part of the student. Each type of problem is presented as an independent unit. The order of study of the types of problems is therefore immaterial and may be adapted readily to any course of instruction.

In the fourth edition chapters have been added on oxidation-reduction reactions involving titration in solution, nuclear chemistry, chemical units involving mass, the significance of chemical formulas, and an introductory chapter outlining the general objectives of the book. Problems involving the gaseous state are presented from the viewpoint of the kinetic-molecular theory of matter. Answers are given to most of the problems.

The author is greatly indebted to the many coworkers who submitted criticisms of earlier editions of the book; to Dr. Glen Wakeham, Associate Professor of Chemistry at the University of Colorado, for a critical review of the manuscript; to Mr. A. G. Clark, Head of the Department of Mathematics of Colorado A & M College; and to Dr. G. H. Whiteford, Head of the Department of Chemistry of Colorado A & M College, for aid and encouragement during preparation of the manuscript.

Paul R. Frey

Colorado A & M College

Table of Contents

Tabulated Bibliography
of Standard Textbooks

The following list gives the author, title, publisher, and date of the standard textbooks referred to in the table on the six succeeding pages.

Babor, Joseph A. *Basic College Chemistry.* Second ed. Crowell, 1953.

Babor, Joseph A., and Lehrman, Alexander. *General College Chemistry.* Third ed. Crowell, 1951.

Babor, Joseph A., and Lehrman, Alexander. *Introductory College Chemistry.* Second ed. Crowell, 1950.

Barker, John W., and Glasoe, Paul K. *First Year College Chemistry.* McGraw-Hill, 1951.

Bogert, L. Jean. *Fundamentals of Chemistry.* Seventh ed. Saunders, 1953.

Brescia, Frank. *General College Chemistry.* Blakiston, 1953.

Brinkley, Stuart R. *Principles of General Chemistry.* Fourth ed. Macmillan, 1951.

Briscoe, H. T. *College Chemistry.* Fourth ed. Houghton Mifflin, 1951.

Briscoe, H. T. *General Chemistry for Colleges.* Fourth ed. Houghton Mifflin, 1949.

Cragg, L. G., and Graham, R. P. *Introduction to the Principles of Chemistry.* Rinehart, 1955.

Cavelti, John E. *Introductory General Chemistry.* Blakiston, 1952.

Deming, H. G. *General Chemistry.* Sixth ed. Wiley, 1952.

Elder, Albert L., Scott, Eding C., and Kanda, Frank A. *Textbook of Chemistry.* Revised ed. Harper, 1948.

Ehret, W. F. *Smith's Introductory College Chemistry.* Third ed. Appleton-Century-Crofts, 1950.

Felsing, William A., and Watt, George W. *General Chemistry.* Third ed. McGraw-Hill, 1951.

Frey, Paul R. *College Chemistry.* Prentice-Hall, 1952.

Gaines, P. C., Binder, Laurence O., Jr., and Woodriff, Ray. *Introduction to Modern Chemistry.* Mosby, 1951.

Garrett, Alfred B., Haskins, Joseph F., and Sisler, Harry H. *Essentials of Chemistry.* Ginn, 1951.

Hildebrand, Joel H., and Powell, Richard E. *Principles of Chemistry.* Sixth ed. Macmillan, 1952.

Holmes, Harry N. *Introductory College Chemistry.* Fifth ed. Macmillan, 1951.

Holmes, Harry N. *General Chemistry.* Fifth ed. Macmillan, 1949.

Hopkins, B. Smith, and Bailar, John C., Jr. *General Chemistry for Colleges.* Fifth ed. Heath, 1956.

Jones, W. N. *General Chemistry.* McGraw-Hill, 1954.

King, G. Brooks, and Caldwell, William E. *The Fundamentals of College Chemistry.* Second ed. American Book Co., 1954.

Luder, W. F., Vernon, and Zuffanti. *General Chemistry.* Saunders, 1953.

Mack, Edward, Jr., Garrett, Alfred B., Haskins, Joseph F., and Verhoek, Frank H. *Textbook of Chemistry*. Ginn, 1956.

McPherson, Henderson, Fernelius, and Quill. *College Chemistry*. Ginn, 1946.

Markham, Edwin, and Smith, Sherman. *General Chemistry*. Houghton, 1954.

Parks, Lytle Raymond, and Steinbach, Warren H. *Systematic College Chemistry*. McGraw-Hill, 1952.

Pauling, Linus. *College Chemistry*. Second ed. Freeman, 1955.

Pauling, Linus. *General Chemistry*. Second ed. Freeman, 1953.

Ritter, H. L. *Introduction to Chemistry*. Wiley, 1955.

Rochow and Wilson. *General Chemistry*. Wiley, 1955.

Sanderson, R. T. *Introduction to Chemistry*. Wiley, 1954.

Scarlett, A. J. *College Chemistry*. Holt, 1956.

Scarlett, A. J., and Gomez-Ibanez. *General College Chemistry*. Holt, 1954.

Selwood, P. W. *General Chemistry*. Revised ed. Holt, 1955.

Sisler, Harry H., Vanderwerf, Calvin A., and Davidson, Arthur W. *College Chemistry*. Macmillan, 1953.

Sisler, Harry H., Vanderwerf, Calvin A., and Davidson, Arthur W. *General Chemistry*. Macmillan, 1949.

Sorum, Clarence H. *General Chemistry*. Prentice-Hall, 1955.

Steiner, Luke E., and Campbell, James E. *General Chemistry*. Macmillan, 1955.

Timm, John Arrend. *General Chemistry*. Third ed. McGraw-Hill, 1956.

Young, L. E., and Porter, C. W. *General Chemistry, A First Course*. Third ed. Prentice-Hall, 1950.

Watt, George W., and Hatch, Lewis F. *The Science of Chemistry*. Second ed. McGraw-Hill, 1954.

QUICK REFERENCE TABLE
TO STANDARD TEXTBOOKS

CHAPTER IN CHEM. PROBS.	TOPIC	BABOR	BABOR & LEHRMAN General	BABOR & LEHRMAN Introd.	BARKER & GLASOE	BOGERT
1	Introduction		1	Introd.	1	1
2	Units of Measurement Used in Chemistry	1 App.	2 App.	2, 6 App.	1, 10	App.
3	Chemical Arithmetic	App.	App.			
4	Significant Digits	App.	App.			
5	Dimensional Quantities			8		
6	The Densities of Substances	2	2, 12	36	1	9
7	Some Quantitative Relationships Involving the Gaseous State	5	2	6	10	
8	Chemical Units Involving Mass	8	3	8	3	3
9	Combining Proportions among the Elements	8	3	3, 11	12	4
10	The Quantitative Significance of Chemical Formulas	8	4	9, 10 11	3, 10 11	5
11	The Quantitative Significance of Chemical Equations	7, 8	4	8, 10	3, 11	5
12	Determination of the Atomic Weights of the Elements	8	3	8	4	2
13	Some Quantitative Relationships Involving Energy		3, 5 12	7, 8 10	9, 12	11
14	A Study of Solutions	15, 20	15, 16	13, 14	13	14, 15
15	Chemical Equilibria	16, 17 20	6, 15 20	12, 25 26	13, 16	14
16	Reactions Involving Oxidation and Reduction	14, 20	23	27, 30	15	12
17	Electrochemistry	18, 21	37	23, 43	15	14
18	Nuclear Chemistry	40	8, 40	19, 21 App.	29	18

···iii–xiv *for list of complete titles.*

TO STANDARD TEXTBOOKS

to chapters

BRESCIA	BRINKLEY	BRISCOE College	BRISCOE General	CAVELTI	CRAGG & GRAHAM	DEMING General	ELDER, SCOTT, & KANDA
1	1	Introd.	Introd.	1	1	1	1
2 App.	App.	7 Introd.	1, 7	6 App.	App.	4, 6 App.	1
				App.		App.	
							4
				App.		6	
	3, 4	13 Introd.	13	2		8	1
2	3	7	7	8	7, 8	8	1, 4
3	1	2, 8	9, 18	4, 9	6	4, 9	4, 12
3, 4	1	2, 8	2, 3 10	22	6	13	2, 12
3, 6	1, 2 3	8, 9	9, 11	4, 9	6	4, 9	4, 8
6	2	9	11	13		4	9
3	5	8	10	4	6	9	12
3, 6 15	4, 5	1, 8 9, 13	10, 11 40	6, 11	6, 14 18	6, 18	12, 13
16, 17	9	15	9, 14 27	22	10, 11	13	14, 16
14, 19	8, 11 12–13	15, 25 26	14, 28 29	22, 25 29	12, 13 15	22, 23	14, 15 17
20	17	21	24	20	16	25	9
18, 22	11, 32	16, 36	27, 40	37	17	43	18
8, 9	33	11	17, 19	42	19, 20	32	38

This table is continued on the following

CHAPTER IN CHEM. PROBS.	TOPIC	EHRET Smith's Introd.	FELSING & WATT	FREY	GAINES, BINDER, & WOODRIFF	GARRETT, HASKINS, & SISLER
1	Introduction	1	1	1	1	1
2	Units of Measurement Used in Chemistry	7 App.	5 App.	1	2 App.	2
3	Chemical Arithmetic			1	2 App.	App.
4	Significant Digits			1	2	App.
5	Dimensional Quantities			1		App.
6	The Densities of Substances	1	6	1	2 App.	6
7	Some Quantitative Relationships Involving the Gaseous State	7	6	9	6	9
8	Chemical Units Involving Mass	11, 14	2, 8	2	3	3
9	Combining Proportions among the Elements	3, 8 9	2	7	9	3
10	The Quantitative Significance of Chemical Formulas	5, 11	2, 3 8	7, 11	3, 6 7	3
11	The Quantitative Significance of Chemical Equations	5, 10 11	2, 3 8	7, 9	8	3 App.
12	Determination of the Atomic Weights of the Elements	11	2, 9	2, 3	7, 9	3
13	Some Quantitative Relationships Involving Energy	4	2, 5	2, 3 7, 8 10, 27	7, 10 12	2, 6 10, 17 35
14	A Study of Solutions	12, 24	10, 11	14	11, 13	11
15	Chemical Equilibria	12, 21 23, 24	12–15	16, 17	12, 14	12
16	Reactions Involving Oxidation and Reduction	26	17	4, 19	16	App.
17	Electrochemistry	22, 46	19	23	13, 34	35
	Nuclear Chemistry	18, 19	30	36	35	16, 17

iii–xiv for list of complete titles.

HILDE-BRAND & POWELL	HOLMES Introd.	HOLMES General	HOPKINS & BAILAR	JONES	KING & CALDWELL	LUDER	MACK et al.
1	1	1	1	1	1	1	1
3	2, 9	1, 7 App.	2 App.	3	2	App.	2
				3		App.	App.
				3			
17		11	2	2	1		2 App.
3	9	7	6	9	8	2	6
1, 2	13	13	2, 3 13	8	8	3	6, 9
6, 9	4	2, 10	3	8	2	3	7, 9
2, 4	5	4, 13	2, 12	8	5, 8	3	3, 10
2, 4	5, 6 8	4, 9	3	8	14	3	9, 10
2	13	13	12		13	3	9
7	7, 10 12–13	5, 13 28	3	8			2, 3 9
4, 6 8	15	15	9, 19	15, 22	15, 18	5, 27	9, 12 14
6, 8 12–14	22, 23 App.	15 21–23	7, 16	21, 22	17, 19	10, 24	24, 25
6, 15	39	10	15		20	12	15
8	21, 46	20, 50	18	17	32	25	13
16	25	27, 28	41	40	31	8	21

This table is continued on the following

CHAPTER IN CHEM. PROBS.	TOPICS	McPHERSON et al.	MARKHAM & SMITH	PARKS & STEINBACH	PAULING College	PAULING General
1	Introduction	1	1		1	1
2	Units of Measurement Used in Chemistry	2 App.	3	Introd.	1 App.	1, 2
3	Chemical Arithmetic		3	App.		
4	Significant Digits		3			
5	Dimensional Quantities		3			1
6	The Densities of Substances	2	3	Introd.	1	
7	Some Quantitative Relationships Involving the Gaseous State	6	5, 6	2	9	14
8	Chemical Units Involving Mass	8	10, 11	4	8	4
9	Combining Proportions among the Elements	7, 8	27	4	8	7
10	The Quantitative Significance of Chemical Formulas	9	11, 13	4, 5	8, 9	7, 14
11	The Quantitative Significance of Chemical Equations	4, 9	13	5	8	7
12	Determination of the Atomic Weights of the Elements	8	23, 27	4	8, 9	7, 14
13	Some Quantitative Relationships Involving Energy	11	11, 36	4, 16	23	1, 14 31
14	A Study of Solutions	14, 16	23, 26	10	18, 20	16
15	Chemical Equilibria	20	24, 32 37	12, 13 14	19, 20 21, 23	19, 20 21, 22
16	Reactions Involving Oxidation and Reduction		22, 27	8	12	11
17	Electrochemistry	31	27, 40	11, 15	10	13
18	Nuclear Chemistry	17	51	6	32	33

xiii–xiv for list of complete titles.

RITTER	ROCHOW & WILSON	SANDER-SON	SCARLETT	SCARLETT & GOMEZ-IBANEZ	SELWOOD	SISLER et al. College
1	1	1	1	1	1	1
1 App.		4	App.	App.	1 App.	1, 2 App.
App.	App.		App.	App.	4	
	App.					
1		3	1		3 App.	1
3	5	13	8	3, 5	5	2
4	1, 5	5	2	2	4, 6	4
9	1	5, 20	2, 11	2	6	4
3, 5	1, 5	5, 13	2	2, 4	4	4, 5
7	1	5	6, 12	2, 4	4, 6	5
5	5		11	4	6	4
13	15	7	1, 6 11	2, 9 37	10	1 3–5
4, 8 9	7	15	13, 15	7, 9	11, 12	13
10, 11	8, 12	16, 18	14, 16	16, 17 18	23	12 15–16
12	9	9	17	15	23	9, 20
13	14	11, 21	15, 25	14, 19	20	14
27	27	27	34	39	24, 25	38

This table is continued on the follow

QUICK REFERENCE TABLE
TO STANDARD TEXTBOOKS (Continued)

CHAPTER IN CHEM. PROBS.	TOPIC	SISLER et al. General	SORUM	STEINER & CAMP-BELL	TIMM	YOUNG & PORTER	WATT & HATCH
1	Introduction	1	1	1	1	1	1
2	Units of Measurement Used in Chemistry	2 App.	1	App.	5 App.	App.	2 App.
3	Chemical Arithmetic				App.		
4	Significant Digits			4			
5	Dimensional Quantities						
6	The Densities of Substances	2	1	2		2	7
7	Some Quantitative Relationships Involving the Gaseous State	3	2	9	4	2	7
8	Chemical Units Involving Mass	6	1	5	6	1	3
9	Combining Proportions among the Elements	5, 6	1, 5 13	4	6, 7	5	
10	The Quantitative Significance of Chemical Formulas	6, 7	1, 4	5	6, 7	5	3
11	The Quantitative Significance of Chemical Equations	7	1, 5	5	13	3, 5	3
12	Determination of the Atomic Weights of the Element	6	2	9	6	5	
13	Some Quantitative Relationships Involving Energy	2, 4 6–8	3	3, 5 8, 11	15	3	2
14	A Study of Solutions	16	11, 13	17	20, 23	4	12, 14
15	Chemical Equilibria	15 18–19	10, 12 14	18, 23	21, 22 23, 26	4	
16	Reactions Involving Oxidation and Reduction	12	16	19	30	8	
17	Electrochemistry	17, 24	15	15, 26	30	15	18
8	Nuclear Chemistry	8	8, 36	13, 21	45, 46	20	5

This table begins on p. xvi.

CHEMISTRY PROBLEMS

AND HOW TO SOLVE THEM

1

Introduction

Chemistry deals with the composition and properties of matter. Under similar conditions such properties never vary for a given substance. For example, water consists of 88.8 per cent oxygen and 11.2 per cent hydrogen by weight, regardless of the source of the water. At sea level the boiling point of water is 100° C. and the freezing point is 0° C. This constancy of the composition and properties of substances, and the unvarying laws of nature, have made chemistry an exact science.

Because chemistry is an exact science, mathematical problems have become an integral part of a course in general chemistry. Most natural laws may be expressed in the form of mathematical formulas, thus introducing the quantitative aspect of the laws. Most of our actions in everyday life are governed by natural laws, and are therefore quantitative. For example, we drive up to a filling station and buy 10 gallons of gasoline at 28 cents per gallon. The car may have cost $2876.32 and will average 17 miles per gallon at a speed of 50 miles per hour.

The whole economy of the chemical industry of the world is based upon the constancy of chemical reactions — the fact that a given chemical reaction involves definite quantities of reacting substances to produce given quantities of products. The industrial chemist must calculate the amounts of iron ore and coke needed to yield a calculated amount of iron. Such calculations are a part of a course in chemistry.

Very few of the mathematical problems given in a course in general chemistry require a knowledge of mathematics beyond that encountered in an elementary course in algebra for their solution. Actually, most of the problems may be solved by proportion methods. The key to the solution of a problem in chemistry lies in a thorough understanding of the chemical principles involved. It is then a matter taking what is given in the problem and, by application of principles, obtaining the desired answer. One should be visualize the problem. If the problem involves 200 ml. of a liquid, a mental picture of it should be formed. No attempt should be made to solve a problem without a thorough understanding of the units used, the terms used, and the chemical principles involved. The solution to the problem then resolves itself into a simple mathematical procedure.

2

Units of Measurement Used in Chemistry

The metric system of measure and the centigrade scale of temperature are used almost exclusively in chemistry. Every student therefore must be familiar with these units of measure. It is for this reason that a survey is given at this time of the common metric units involving length, weight, and volume, and a comparison of the Fahrenheit, centigrade, and absolute scales of temperature. Table 2.4, which gives the relationship between corresponding English and metric units, will be found helpful in visualizing the relative magnitude of the more commonly used metric units.

Metric Units of Length, Mass, and Volume

2.1. Introduction. In any system of measurement there must be arbitrarily established units of *length*, *mass*, and *volume*. Examination of the apparatus used in laboratories will show that length is commonly measured in *meters*, mass in *grams*, and volume in *cubic centimeters* or *milliliters*. These are the fundamental units of length, mass, and volume in the metric system.

Metric units are based on a decimal system in which the prefix designates the multiple or submultiple value of the quantity in terms of the fundamental unit.

TABLE 2.1

PREFIXES USED IN THE METRIC SYSTEM AND THEIR VALUES

micro =	0.000001	part of fundamental unit
milli =	0.001	part of fundamental unit
centi =	0.01	part of fundamental unit
deci =	0.1	part of fundamental unit
	1.0	fundamental unit
deka =	10	times fundamental unit
hecto =	100	times fundamental unit
kilo =	1000	times fundamental unit

The principal advantage of the metric system is that values of length, mass, and volume repeat in multiples of ten. English units are inconsistent — 12 in. equals one foot, 3 ft. equals one yard, and $5\frac{1}{2}$ yd. equals one rod. The metric system also represents a more international standard than does the English system. The meter, gram, and liter as used in the United States are identical to the corresponding units used in any other country. On the other hand, in England a quart is larger than the quart used in the United States, and in France an inch is longer than the inch used in England.

The *centimeter-gram-second* (cgs) system, called the *metric* system, and the *foot-pound-second* (fps) system, called the *English* system, are the two principal surviving standards in the world today. The unit of time, the *second*, is the same in each of the two systems.

2.2. The More Commonly Used Metric Units of Length. The fundamental unit of length in the metric system is the *meter* (m.). Originally the meter was intended to represent one ten-millionth of the earth's quadrant. Although recent measurements with more precise measuring instruments than used originally have shown the meter to be slightly in error, the length as originally adopted has been retained. The meter is now defined as the distance between two parallel lines on a platinum-iridium bar kept in the International Bureau of Weights and Measures at Sèvres, France. Replicas of the bar are called secondary standards and are available to any country desiring them. The United States possesses two such secondary standards of the meter which, along with other standards, are kept in the National Bureau of Standards, Washington, D.C. In Tables 2.2 and 2.3, the more commonly used units are given in **boldface** type.

TABLE 2.2

METRIC UNITS OF LENGTH USING THE METER AS THE FUNDAMENTAL UNIT

10 **millimeters** (mm.)	= 1 **centimeter** (cm.)
10 centimeters	= 1 decimeter (dm.)
10 decimeters	= 1 **meter**
10 meters	= 1 dekameter (dkm.)
10 dekameters	= 1 hectometer (hm.)
10 hectometers	= 1 **kilometer** (km.)

2.3. The More Commonly Used Metric Units of Mass. The fundamental unit of mass in the metric system is the *gram* (g.). The gram · originally intended to represent the volume occupied by 1 cm.³ ·er at 3.98° C., the temperature at which water possesses its greatest density. As with the meter, later measurements have shown that one gram of water at 3.98° C. occupies a volume of 1.000027 cm.³ It is only in extremely accurate work that this discrepancy in volume must be taken into consideration.

A direct relationship thus exists between the centimeter as a unit of length and the gram as a unit of mass. Table 2.3 gives metric units of mass in terms of decimal fractions of a gram because of the common practice of recording weights in this manner.

TABLE 2.3
METRIC UNITS OF MASS

1 milligram (mg.)	=	0.001	g.
1 centigram (cg.)	=	0.01	g.
1 decigram (dg.)	=	0.1	g.
1 gram (g.)	=	1	g.
1 kilogram (kg.)	=	1000	g.

2.4. The More Commonly Used Metric Units of Volume. Units of area and volume in the metric system are obtained in the same manner as are corresponding units in the English system.

The *cubic centimeter* (cc. or cm.³) is the metric unit of volume most commonly used in laboratory work. It is, however, a relatively small unit of volume. A larger unit of volume, the *liter* (l.), is defined as the volume occupied by one kilogram of water at 3.98° C. The liter was also designed to correct for the error involved when the cubic centimeter was adopted. One liter is therefore equal to 1000.027 cm.³ Ordinarily in the laboratory it is assumed that one milliliter (ml.) is equal in volume to one cubic centimeter. That is, cc., cm.³, and ml. may be used interchangeably.

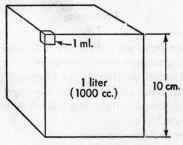

Fig. 2.1. The metric unit
of volume, the liter.

2.5. The Relationship between English and Metric Units of Length, Mass, and Volume. By means of constants such as given in Table 2.4, one may change values in one system of units into the corresponding values in the other system of units.

TABLE 2.4

CONSTANTS RELATING ENGLISH AND METRIC UNITS

A[1]	c		B
inches	×	2.54	= centimeters
meters	×	1.094	= yards
liters	×	61.0	= cubic inches
liters	×	1.06	= quarts
pounds	×	454	= grams
kilograms	×	2.20	= pounds

$$^1 \; A = \frac{B}{c}, \text{ and } B = A \times c.$$

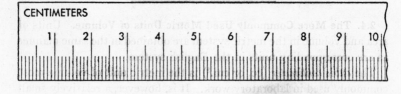

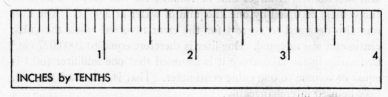

Fig. 2.2. A comparison of the English and metric units of length.

Problems

2.1. Mental exercises:

    a. How many micrograms are there in one milligram?

    b. How many milligrams are there in 0.1 gram?

    c. How many milligrams are there in one kilogram?

    d. How many centimeters are there in one kilometer?

    e. How many milliliters are there in a rod which measures 10 cm. by 10 cm. by 100 cm.?

2.2. List in the order of increasing value:

    a. Units of length — foot, meter, kilometer, yard, mile, millimeter, inch, and centimeter.

b. Units of mass — kilogram, ounce, milligram, pound, and gram.

c. Units of volume — milliliter, quart, cubic centimeter, cubic inch, cubic decimeter, and liter.

2.3. Calculate your height in meters and in centimeters.

2.4. Calculate your weight in grams and in kilograms.

2.5. What is the weight of one quart of water in grams?   *Ans.* 943 g.

2.6. How many liters are there in five gallons?   *Ans.* 18.9 l.

2.7. Calculate the volume in liters of a box 12 cm. by 3.5 cm. by 150 cm.
          Ans. 6.3 l.

2.8. What is the length of a foot rule in millimeters?   *Ans.* 305 mm.

2.9. How many liters are there in one cubic meter?   *Ans.* 1000 l.

2.10. Calculate the volume in liters of a box 24 in. long, 12 in. wide, and 12 in. high.   *Ans.* 56.6 l.

2.11. A uniform iron bar 15 in. long weighs 2 lb. 4 oz. Calculate the weight of the bar in grams per centimeter of length.   *Ans.* 26.8 g.

2.12. Which is the heavier, 100 marbles each of which weighs 10 g., or 200 marbles each of which weighs 0.1 oz.?

2.13. How many kilograms are there in one ton?   *Ans.* 909 kg.

2.14. If sugar costs 8 cents per pound, what is its cost per 100 grams?
          Ans. $0.0176.

2.15. How many cubic inches are there in one liter?

2.16. If gasoline costs 10 cents per liter in Mexico and 30 cents per gallon in the United States, which is the cheaper?

Temperature Scales

2.6. Introduction. In the laboratory, temperatures are usually recorded as *centigrade* (° C.) or *absolute* (° K.). The symbol K. for absolute temperatures is used in honor of Lord Kelvin, the first person to postulate the existence of such a scale and its possible use. The *Fahrenheit* (° F.) scale is used domestically and, to some extent, in industry in the United States and England. The mercury expansion type of thermometer is the most commonly used instrument to measure temperatures.

2.7. Interconversion of Centigrade and Absolute Temperatures. In the solution of mathematical problems it is common practice to represent absolute temperatures by T and centigrade temperatures by t in formulas involving the quantities.

From Fig. 2.3 it will be observed that for any given temperature the values in ° C. and ° K. differ by the constant value 273. This constant difference is due to the choice of the zero point on each of the two scales. That is:

$$T = 273 + t$$

or $$t = T - 273.$$

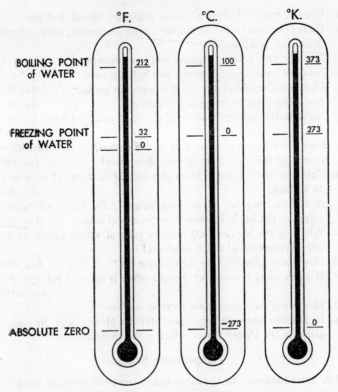

Fig. 2.3. A comparison of the Fahrenheit, centigrade, and absolute scales of temperature.

Example 2.1. Normal body temperature is about 37° C. What would this be on the absolute scale?

Solution.

$$T = 273 + t$$

or

$$T = 273 + 37$$
$$= 310° K.$$

2.8. Interconversion of Fahrenheit and Centigrade Temperatures. The interconversion of Fahrenheit and centigrade temperatures is based upon the relationship shown in Fig. 2.3. That is:

$$180° F. = 100° C.$$

or

$$1° F. = (\tfrac{5}{9})° C.$$

and

$$1° C. = (\tfrac{9}{5})° F.$$

Example 2.2.   Convert 86° F. to the corresponding centigrade value.

Solution.   Let us see how we may reason out the answer to the problem. First, choose a reference temperature such as the boiling point of water as shown in Fig. 2.4.   The solution to the problem now lies in converting the Fahrenheit scale interval "a" to the corresponding centigrade scale interval "b."   The temperature to be found is "c," which is $100 - b$.

$$a = 212 - 86 = 126,$$
$$b = 126 \times \tfrac{5}{9} = 70,$$
and
$$c = 100 - 70 = 30° \text{ C.}$$

That is, 86° F. is equal to 30° C.

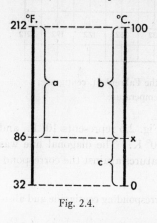

Fig. 2.4.

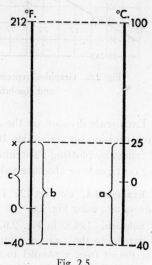

Fig. 2.5.

Example 2.3.   Convert 25° C. to the corresponding Fahrenheit value.

Solution.   It so happens that −40° C. and −40° F. are the same temperature.   Using −40° C. as the reference temperature we see, from Fig. 2.5, that:

$$a = 40 + 25 = 65,$$
$$b = 65 \times \tfrac{9}{5} = 117,$$
and
$$c = 117 - 40 = 77° \text{ F.}$$

That is, 25° C. is equal to 77° F.

2.9. The Interconversion of Fahrenheit, Centigrade, and Absolute Temperatures by Means of a Graphical Method.   The interconversion of the three scales of temperature may be brought about by means of the graph shown in Fig. 2.6.

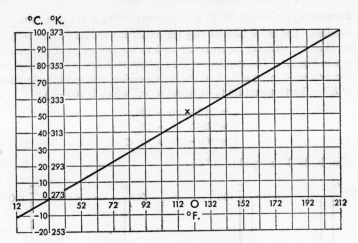

Fig. 2.6.   Graphical representation of the Fahrenheit, centigrade, and absolute scales of temperature.

Each scale division on the x-axis in Fig. 2.6 represents 10° F., and each division on the y-axis 10° C. or 10° K. The diagonal line was obtained by plotting Fahrenheit temperatures against the corresponding centigrade or absolute values.

Example 2.4. Convert 122° F. to the corresponding centigrade and absolute values, using Fig. 2.6.

Solution. Let O in Fig. 2.6 represent 122° F. Now draw a line from O parallel to the y-axis and intersecting the diagonal at x. A horizontal line drawn from x parallel to the x-axis intersects the y-axis at a point corresponding to 50° C. or 323° K. These are the temperatures to be found.

Problems

2.17. Convert:
     a. 50° C. to ° F.   *Ans.* 122° F.
     b. 50° F. to ° C.   *Ans.* 10° C.
     c. 50° F. to ° K.   *Ans.* 283° K.
     d. 50° K. to ° F.   *Ans.* −369° F.

2.18. A solution of salt water was found to freeze at −12° F. What is the freezing point of the solution in ° C.?   *Ans.* −24.4° C.

2.19. Mercury boils at 630° K. Calculate the boiling point of mercury in (a) ° C., and (b) ° F.   *Ans.* (a) 357° C.
                                                           (b) 675° F.

2.20. Assuming the surface of the sun to be 10.832° F., calculate the temperature in ° K.   *Ans.* 6273° K.

2.21. By means of Fig. 2.6 convert: (a) 50° C. to ° F., (b) 50° F. to ° C., (c) 50° F. to ° K., and (d) 50° K. to ° F.   *Ans.* (a) 122° F.

                                                 (b) 10° C.

                                                 (c) 283° K.

                                                 (d) −369° F.

2.22. Show that Fahrenheit and centigrade temperatures are the same at −40 degrees.

3

Chemical Arithmetic

A knowledge of arithmetic and elementary algebra is necessary in order to solve problems in chemistry. The brief review given of negative quantities, fractions, exponential quantities, and unknown quantities occurring in equations will recall to the student their meaning and usage. Ratio and proportion are explained, these being fundamental concepts in the treatment of most problems in chemistry.

Negative Quantities and Fractions

3.1. The Use of Negative Quantities. When a negative number is involved in the process of addition, it is equivalent to subtracting the quantity. For example:

$$276 + (-132) + 321 = 276 - 132 + 321 = 465.$$

When a negative number is involved in the process of subtraction, it is equivalent to adding the quantity. For example:

$$276 - (-132) + 321 = 276 + 132 + 321 = 729.$$

3.2. The Use of Common Fractions. Fractions must be reduced to a common denominator before they are added or subtracted. For example:

$$\frac{3}{4} - 2\frac{1}{6} + 7\frac{5}{12} = \frac{3}{4} - \frac{13}{6} + \frac{89}{12} = \frac{9 - 26 + 89}{12} = \frac{72}{12} = 6.$$

When multiplying two or more fractions, multiply the numerators for a new numerator, and the denominators for a new denominator; then reduce the resulting fraction to its lowest terms. For example:

$$176 \times \frac{298}{273} \times \frac{735}{760} = \frac{176 \times 298 \times 735}{273 \times 760} = 186.$$

When dividing one fraction by another, invert the divisor and multiply. For example:

$$6\tfrac{1}{2} \div \tfrac{3}{4} = \tfrac{13}{2} \times \tfrac{4}{3} = \tfrac{52}{6} = 8\tfrac{2}{3}.$$

12

Only common factors may be canceled in the numerator and denominator of a fraction. For example:

$$36 \times \frac{18}{72 \times 18} \times \frac{24 + 6}{24} = \frac{36 \times \cancel{18} \times (24 + 6)}{72 \times \cancel{18} \times 24} = \frac{36 \times 30}{72 \times 24} = \frac{5}{8}.$$

Observe that the 24 occurring in both the numerator and denominator is not a common factor and therefore cannot be canceled.

3.3. The Treatment of Decimal Fractions in Mathematical Operations. When adding or subtracting decimal fractions, the decimal points must be in a vertical column. For example:

$$\begin{array}{r} 16.34 \\ 176.00 \\ 3.41 \\ \hline 195.75 \end{array}$$

The product of two decimal fractions contains as many decimal places as the sum of the decimal places in the two quantities multiplied. For example:

$$7.3\underline{3} \times 4.\underline{7} = 34.\underline{451}.$$

The quotient of two decimal fractions contains as many decimal places as there are places in the dividend minus the number in the divisor. For example:

$$\begin{array}{r} 28.4\overline{\smash{)}\,258.986}\underline{|\,9.12} \\ 255\,6 \\ \hline 3\,38 \\ 2\,84 \\ \hline 546 \\ 568 \\ \hline \end{array}$$

To change a common fraction to a decimal fraction, divide the numerator by the denominator. For example:

$$\tfrac{11}{36} = 0.31.$$

Zero may not be used as a divisor in a mathematical operation.

3.4. The Meaning of Percentage. A decimal fraction indicates a given portion of a unit value, whereas percentage indicates the number of parts out of 100. A decimal fraction may therefore be converted to percentage by multiplying by 100. For example:

$$0.32 \times 100 = 32\%.$$

Problems

3.1. Simplify:
- a. $342 - (-81)$.
- b. $964 - (126 - 38)$.
- c. $(1.8 \times 24) + 32$.
- d. $1.8 \times (24 + 32)$.

3.2. Perform the indicated operations and reduce to the lowest terms:
- a. $3\frac{3}{4} + 5\frac{7}{9}$
- b. $1\frac{3}{7} \times \frac{1}{5}$
- c. $6\frac{5}{8} - 1\frac{3}{7}$
- d. $1\frac{2}{5} \div \frac{3}{7}$
- e. $\dfrac{273 + 20}{273 + 90} \times \dfrac{4}{5}$
- f. $\dfrac{231 \times 6}{6} + \dfrac{18 + 3}{3}$
- g. $\dfrac{124}{760} \times \dfrac{760}{740} \times \dfrac{273 + 18}{273}$
- h. $\dfrac{3\frac{1}{3} \times 2\frac{3}{4}}{3} \div 4\frac{1}{7}$

3.3. Change the following to decimal fractions:
- a. $\frac{4}{5}$
- b. $1\frac{4}{5}$
- c. $\dfrac{2.125}{0.27}$
- d. $\frac{1}{3}$

3.4. Express each of the following as per cent:
- a. 0.06
- b. 0.1
- c. 3.74
- d. $\frac{6}{100}$
- e. $\frac{23}{25}$
- f. $1\frac{3}{4}$

3.5. Express each of the following as decimal fractions:
- a. 16%
- b. 1.2%
- c. 0.3%
- d. $16\frac{2}{3}\%$
- e. 20%
- f. $\frac{1}{4}\%$

3.6. What is 15 per cent of \$240?	*Ans.* 36.
3.7. What is 2.5 per cent of \$1500?	*Ans.* 37.5.
3.8. What is $2\frac{1}{4}$ per cent of \$1000?	*Ans.* 22.5.
3.9. What is 0.02 per cent of \$2500?	*Ans.* 0.50.

Exponential Quantities

3.5. Introduction. In scientific work it is frequently necessary to use quite large numbers, such as 602,000,000,000,000,000,000,000, or extremely small numbers, such as 0.00000000048. A method whereby such numbers may be written in a more condensed form will be presented. For example, 10,000 may be written 10^4 where 4 is the exponent to the *base* 10. Table 3.1 gives several other powers of ten. It is evident that the table could be extended indefinitely.

ZERO AS AN EXPONENT

TABLE 3.1

SOME POWERS OF TEN

$10^3 = 1000$	$10^0 = 1$
$10^2 = 100$	$10^{-1} = 0.1$
$10^1 = 10$	$10^{-2} = 0.01$

Numbers other than 10 may be used as a base. For example, $3^2 = 9$ and $7^2 = 49$. The base 10 is the most convenient to use, particularly in elementary work involving exponential expressions. Subsequent material will be limited to the use of 10 as a base.

3.6. Zero as an Exponent. Any number to the exponent zero is equal to one. That is, $x^0 = 1$. It is important to remember this fact since zero frequently occurs as an exponent in mathematical expressions.

3.7. Negative Exponents. Any quantity expressed in the negative exponential form may be written as the reciprocal of the number with the sign of the exponent changed. That is:

$$x^{-a} = \frac{1}{x^a}, \quad 10^{-1} = \frac{1}{10}, \quad \text{and} \quad 10^{-5} = \frac{1}{10^5}.$$

3.8. Numbers Expressed as a Power of Ten. The question now arises as to how a number such as 600 may be expressed as a power of ten. Since $10^2 = 100$ and $10^3 = 1000$, it is evident that a fractional exponent having a value between 2 and 3 must be used to express 600 as a power of ten. That is, in the expression $10^x = 600$, x has a value between 2 and 3. Methods for calculating such values will be found in most algebra texts. In this particular case $x = 2.7782$. That is, $10^{2.7782} = 600$.

It is also possible to express a number such as 600 as the product of two numbers, one of which is an integer power of ten. That is:

$$600 = 6 \times 100 = 6 \times 10^2.$$

Use may be made of negative exponents in expressing a quantity such as 0.00009 as a power of ten.

$$0.00009 = \frac{9}{100,000} = 9 \times \frac{1}{100,000} = 9 \times \frac{1}{10^5} = 9 \times 10^{-5}.$$

Numbers such as 674,000 may be expressed as a power of ten in any one of a number of ways, its being purely a matter of choice as to which expression is used.

$$674,000 = 674 \times 1000 \quad = 674 \times 10^3.$$
$$674,000 = 67.4 \times 10,000 \; = 67.4 \times 10^4.$$
$$674,000 = 6.74 \times 100,000 = 6.74 \times 10^5.$$

3.9. The Addition and Subtraction of Exponential Quantities. In order to add or subtract exponential quantities, each number must be expressed to the same power and referred to the same base. For example:

$$10^3 + 10^3 = 2 \times 10^3.$$

The above limitations greatly restrict the use of exponents in the operations of addition and subtraction. In fact, exponential expressions are seldom used in such mathematical operations.

3.10. The Multiplication and Division of Exponential Quantities. In order to multiply or divide exponential quantities, each number needs only to be referred to the same base. Exponential quantities will therefore be found quite useful in simplifying the operations of multiplication and division. In multiplication the exponents are added. For example:

$$10^2 \times 10^3 = 10^{2+3} = 10^5.$$

In division the exponent of the divisor is subtracted from that of the dividend. For example:

$$10^7 \div 10^3 = 10^{7-3} = 10^4.$$

Example 3.1. Multiply 3200 by 75,000.

Solution.

$$3200 \times 75,000 = 3.2 \times 10^3 \times 7.5 \times 10^4$$
$$= (3.2 \times 7.5)(10^3 \times 10^4)$$
$$= 24 \times 10^7.$$

Observe that rearranging the order in which a series of numbers are multiplied does not change the answer.

Example 3.2. Divide 0.0035 by 0.00078.

Solution.

$$\frac{0.0035}{0.00078} = \frac{3.5 \times 10^{-3}}{7.8 \times 10^{-4}} = 0.45 \times 10^{-3-(-4)} = 0.45 \times 10 = 4.5.$$

Example 3.3. Simplify $\dfrac{0.088 \times 760 \times 220,000}{4400}$.

Solution.

$$\frac{0.088 \times 760 \times 220{,}000}{4400} = \frac{(8.8 \times 10^{-2})(7.6 \times 10^{2})(2.2 \times 10^{5})}{(4.4 \times 10^{3})}$$

$$= \frac{(8.8 \times 7.6 \times 2.2)(10^{-2} \times 10^{2} \times 10^{5})}{(4.4 \times 10^{3})}$$

$$= \frac{147}{4.4} \times 10^{-2+2+5-3}$$

$$= 33.4 \times 10^{2}.$$

3.11. The Use of Exponential Quantities in Evaluating an Answer.
In problems involving the successive multiplication and division of
numbers, there is always the possibility of misplacing the decimal
point in the answer. In such problems one may determine by inspection whether or not the answer is of the proper order of magnitude.

Example 3.4. Determine whether or not the decimal point is properly
located in the following answer:

$$76.5 \times \frac{120 \times 1600}{2000 \times 273} = 269.$$

Solution. This method involves what is termed "approximation of
numbers." Each number other than the power of ten is changed to the
nearest integer value. Then:

$$\frac{(7.65 \times 10)(1.20 \times 10^{2})(1.6 \times 10^{3})}{(2.000 \times 10^{3})(2.73 \times 10^{2})} \quad \text{becomes}$$

$$\frac{(8 \times 10)(1 \times 10^{2})(2 \times 10^{3})}{(2 \times 10^{3})(3 \times 10^{2})} = \frac{16 \times 10^{6}}{6 \times 10^{5}} = 3 \times 10 = 30.$$

The correct answer is of the order of magnitude of 30. Evidently an
error has been made in the location of the decimal point, the correct answer
being 26.9. With practice one can readily acquire the ability to carry out
most of the above operations mentally.

**3.12. A Rule for Determining the Numerical Value and Sign of
an Exponent.** By means of the following rule it is possible to determine the numerical value and sign of an exponent when expressing
a number as the product of two other numbers, one of which is an
integer power of ten. *Rule:* A shift of the decimal point to the right
requires the use of a negative exponent; to the left, a positive exponent. In either case the exponent is equal numerically to the number of places the decimal point has been moved. For example:

$$0.0631 = 6.31 \times 10^{-2}, \quad \text{and} \quad 4300 = 4.3 \times 10^{3}.$$
$$\rightarrow \qquad\qquad\qquad\qquad \leftarrow$$

The arrows represent the shift in the decimal point.

Problems

3.10. Mental exercises:

  a. Multiply 255 by 100.

  b. Divide 325 by 100.

  c. Multiply 0.0899 by 1000.

  d. Divide 1.42 by 1000.

  e. Determine the value of x in each of the following:

$$10^x = 10,000; \quad 10^x = 0.0001; \quad 10^3 = x; \quad 10^{-5} = x.$$

3.11. Express each of the following as the product of two numbers, one of which is a power of ten:

  a. 2500   c. 0.000196   e. 0.01

  b. 368,000   d. 0.364   f. 107,000,0C0

3.12. Change to nonexponential form:

  a. 2.3×10^3 c. 2.3×10^{-3} e. 0.0076×10^{-2}

  b. 6.06×10^{23} d. 4.77×10^{-10} f. $\dfrac{23.4}{10^3}$

3.13. Evaluate the following by first converting to the exponential form, as in Example 3.3:

  a. 2000×1000 d. $0.0174 \div 0.009$

  b. $1760 \times 10,760$ e. $760 \times 373 \times 76.4$

  c. $72,400 \div 340$ f. 1.485×0.0096

3.14. Evaluate, using exponential expressions:

  a. $487 \times \frac{760}{640}$ *Ans.* 5.78×10^2.

  b. $\dfrac{73,000 \times 0.00075}{170}$ *Ans.* 3.2×10^{-1}.

  c. $\dfrac{1.27 \times 120,000}{174.5 \times 27.36}$ *Ans.* 3.2×10.

  d. $\dfrac{25.48 \times 368 \times 160}{320,000}$ *Ans.* 4.7.

3.15. By the method of approximation determine the location of the decimal point in each of the following:

  a. $\dfrac{276 \times 1300}{230} = 1560.$ c. $38 \times \frac{735}{760} \times \frac{899}{273} = 4038.$

  b. $\dfrac{1600 \times 4.6}{486 \times 76.5} = 1978.$ d. $\dfrac{341 \times 0.00782}{1742 \times 3.07} = 4987.$

3.16. Express exponentially the number of seconds in one year.

                                              Ans. 3.1536×10^7.

3.17. Express exponentially the number of miles in one light year, given that light travels at the rate of 186,000 miles per second.   *Ans.* 5.87×10^{12}.

3.18. Calculate the number of centuries in one second. *Ans.* 3.17×10^{-10}.

3.19. How many grams of water are there in one cubic kilometer of water?

Ans. 10^{15}.

Expressions Involving Unknown Quantities

3.13. Algebraic Equations. Only coefficients of like factors may be added or subtracted. For example:

$$13x + 9y - 2y = 13x + 7y.$$

Exponents of like factors are added when exponential quantities are multiplied, and subtracted when exponential quantities are divided. For example:

$$6y \times 2ay^2 = 12ay^3$$

and

$$12ax^2 \div 6x = \frac{12ax^2}{6x} = 2ax^{2-1} = 2ax.$$

First-degree equations are those in which the exponent of the unknown quantity does not exceed unity. For example:

$$36x = 756 + 8x. \quad \text{Collecting like terms gives}$$

or

$$36x - 8x = 756$$

$$28x = 756$$

and

$$x = 27.$$

Second-degree equations are those in which the exponent of the unknown quantity is greater than one but does not exceed two. These are sometimes called *quadratic* equations, and have the general form $ax^2 + bx + c = 0$. A quadratic equation may be solved for x by substituting the values of the constants a, b, and c in the formula:

$$x = \frac{-b \pm \sqrt{b^2 - 4ac}}{2a}.$$

Example 3.5. Solve for x, given that $9x^2 + 5x - 8 = 0$.
Solution.

$$x = \frac{-5 \pm \sqrt{5^2 - (4)(9)(-8)}}{(2)(9)}$$

$$= \frac{-5 \pm 18}{18}$$

$$= 0.72 \quad \text{or} \quad -1.3.$$

3.14. The Use of Proportion in Solving Problems. A proportion is an expression of equality between two ratios. For example, given that:

$$\frac{122}{11.2} = \frac{24}{x}$$

then $122x = (11.2)(24)$

and $x = 2.2.$

Example 3.6. A sample of brass weighing 4.537 g. was found to contain 3.172 g. of copper. How much copper would there be in 500 g. of the brass?

Solution. The ratio of copper to brass must be a constant. Therefore:

$$\frac{3.172 \text{ g. copper}}{4.537 \text{ g. brass}} = \frac{x \text{ g. copper}}{500 \text{ g. brass}}$$

or $x = \dfrac{(3.172)(500)}{(4.537)}$ g. copper

$$= 350 \text{ g. copper.}$$

Problems

3.20. Solve for x:

a. $3x - 9 = 0.$

b. $\dfrac{16 - x}{x} = 12.$

c. $\frac{273}{293} = x - 4.$

d. $(260)(43 - 21x) = (400)(39.6).$

e. $2x^2 + 5x - 35 = 0.$

f. $\dfrac{122.5}{x} = \dfrac{4.8}{33.4}.$

3.21. An alcohol water mixture contains 20 per cent alcohol by weight. What is the ratio by weight of alcohol to water?

3.22. A sample of brass contains 65 per cent copper and 35 per cent zinc. How much copper would there be in a 4.925 g. sample of the brass?

3.23. If a coiled spring stretches 24 cm. due to a weight of 16 g., how much will it stretch with a weight of 20 g., assuming the stretch to be proportional to the weight?   *Ans.* 30 cm.

4

Significant Digits

In carrying out the mathematical operations of addition, subtraction, multiplication, and division, the student is confronted with the problem of the number of digits to retain in the answer. Very definite rules may be followed in such mathematical operations. Fortunately the rules are not difficult to remember and are easy to apply. Much unnecessary work may be avoided in mathematical operations by remembering the rules applying to significant digits.

An Explanation of Significant Digits

4.1. Introduction. When recording data such as length, weight, volume, or temperature, the data should represent the greatest accuracy possible with the measuring instruments used. Also, the mathematical operations applied to such data should be as accurate as is consistent with the data.

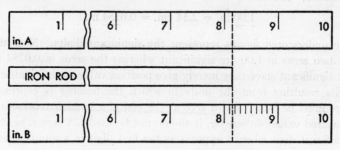

Fig. 4.1. The accuracy of a measurement depends
upon the measuring instrument used.

The last figure in an experimental quantity is usually an estimated one. For example, suppose the length of the iron rod shown in Fig. 4.1 is to be determined using the rule A, in which the inch is the smallest scale division. From Fig. 4.1 we see that the end of the

21

rod lies nearer the 8 than the 9 inch mark. Estimating the length
of the rod to the nearest tenth of an inch gives the value 8.1 in. Now
suppose the length of the rod is again measured, this time with the
rule B, in which a tenth of an inch is the smallest scale division. The
length of the rod lies between 8.1 in. and 8.2 in., the estimated value
being 8.13 in. Note that the underscored figure in each of the measured values is an estimated one.

4.2. The Meaning of Significant Digits. Any figure representing a
measured quantity is a significant digit. For example, the value
8.1 in. for the rod in Fig. 4.1 represents two significant digits, and
the value 8.13 in. represents three significant digits. The number of
significant digits in a quantity is independent of the location of the
decimal point.

From the preceding paragraph it is evident that one factor which
determines the number of significant digits in a quantity is the accuracy
of the measuring instrument. A second factor is the size of the object
measured. For example, suppose each of two coins is weighed on a
balance accurate to one-tenth of a gram. The first coin is found to
weigh 3.3 g. and the second 36.1 g. The first represents two and the
second three significant digits respectively. Because of its larger
mass the second coin is capable of being measured on a given balance
to a greater number of significant digits than is the first coin.

Zero occupies a unique position in our number system, as a result
of which it may or may not be a significant digit when occurring in
a number. For example:

$$1.00 \text{ in.} = 2.54 \text{ cm.} = 0.0254 \text{ m.}$$

The underscored figures represent the significant digits. Note that
the two zeros in 1.00 are significant whereas the zeros in 0.0254 are
not significant since they merely give position value to the significant
digits resulting from the units in which the number is expressed.
Care must be taken that a zero at the end of a number represents a
measured value; otherwise, it should not be used. A zero is never a
significant digit when it appears as the first digit in a number, as in
0.0254 m. Again, the statement that 1.00 m. = 1.09 yd. represents
three significant digits for each number. Note that the zero in 1.09 yd.
is used in the same sense as are the other nine symbols — 1, 2, 3, 4,
5, 6, 7, 8, 9.

The foregoing discussion of significant digits is concerned only with
integer values or decimal fractions. The question now arises as to
how we may indicate whether or not the zero in a number such as

80 is a significant digit. The statement that the earth is 7926 miles in diameter at the equator represents four significant digits. However, to state that the earth is approximately 8000 miles in diameter represents but one significant digit. Exponential forms are commonly used to designate whether or not the zeros in such integer values are significant. That is, 8×10^3 miles represents the diameter of the earth to one significant digit. The statement that light travels 1.86×10^5 miles per second represents three significant digits. The significant digits are given in the quantity other than the power of ten. A general rule for determining the number of significant digits is to pick out the first and last figures representing the actual measured quantity; the number of figures between and including these represents the number of significant digits. For example:

$$\overline{7}8.00\underline{3}6 = 6 \text{ significant digits;}$$
$$0.0\underline{1}5\underline{4} = 3 \text{ significant digits.}$$

Some Practical Applications of Significant Digits

4.3. The Use of Significant Digits in Addition and Subtraction. Only quantities representing like units and measured to the same number of decimal places may be added or subtracted, regardless of the number of significant digits in the quantities.

Example 4.1. Add 12.7 m., 219.3 cm., and 332.1 mm.

Solution. Change the quantities to like units, the units used being a matter of choice; drop the underscored figures in order to reduce each value to the same number of decimal places, and add.

$$
\begin{array}{llll}
12.7 \text{ m.} & = 12.7 \text{ m.} & = 12.7 \text{ m.} \\
219.3 \text{ cm.} & = 2.1\underline{93} \text{ m.} & = 2.2 \text{ m.} \\
332.1 \text{ mm.} & = 0.\underline{3321} \text{ m.} & = 0.3 \text{ m.} \\
& & \text{Add} \quad \overline{15.2 \text{ m.}}
\end{array}
$$

Observe that the last figure retained is increased by one if the number immediately following is five or greater. Thus 2.193 becomes 2.2, and 0.3321 becomes 0.3.

4.4. The Use of Significant Digits in Multiplication and Division. In multiplication and division the number of significant digits retained in the product or quotient is equal to the least number of significant digits found in either of the quantities involved.

Example 4.2. Perform the indicated operations:

a. Multiply 16.14 by 5.29.

b. Divide 47.628 by 6.24.

Solution.

a. $16.14 \times 5.29 = 85.3806 = 85.4$.

b. $47.628 \div 6.24 = 7.632 = 7.63$.

4.5. The General Application of Significant Digits. Use of the above simple rules involving addition, subtraction, multiplication, and division will save time and yet give results which are as accurate as the data from which the calculations were made. The rules are particularly helpful where a series of multiplications and divisions are involved.

Example 4.3. Simplify the expression $\dfrac{58 \times 760 \times 273}{755 \times 293}$.

Solution.

$$58 \times 760 = 44000 \text{ (retain 2 significant digits)};$$
$$44000 \times 273 = 12000000 \text{ (retain 2 significant digits)};$$
$$755 \times 293 = 221000 \text{ (retain 3 significant digits)};$$

then $\qquad \dfrac{12000000}{221000} = 54$ (retain 2 significant digits).

Problems

4.1. State the number of significant digits in each of the following:

a. 23 ft.

b. 1.6 m.

c. 322.1 cm.

d. 0.0254 m.

e. 120.2 l.

f. 1.0004 g.

g. 2000.2 m.

h. 0.0010101 kg.

i. 999.0909 ft.

j. 3.24×10^3 cm.

k. 1.60×10^2 g.

l. 1.050×10^{-3} ml.

4.2. Perform the indicated operations:

a. 2.1 m. + 0.3 m. + 2.07 m. + 3.224 m.

b. 21.630 l. + 844 ml. + 0.036 l. + 0.196 ml.

c. 13.22 cm. − 28.36 mm.

d. 0.763 kg. − 32.8 g.

e. 32.57×7.14.

f. 0.0482×0.2134.

g. $7632 \div 173$.

h. $3.438 \div 0.9876$.

4.3. Evaluate to three significant digits:

a. 2143×12.31.

b. 0.5314×0.1132.

c. $0.041761 \div 32.15$.

d. $7612.58 \div 285.7$.

5

Dimensional Quantities

Most numbers express a magnitude relative to some value taken as a standard. A table six feet long is six times the length of an arbitrary standard called a foot. A number of examples are given which stress the importance of the proper use of dimensions in mathematical operations.

An Explanation of Dimensions

5.1. Introduction. By dimensions is meant the units such as grams, pounds, and feet in which a quantity is expressed. The statement that a board is 6 feet long involves two important ideas — the *numerical* value 6 and the *dimensional* value feet, both of which are necessary in order to convey a correct idea of the size of the object. Normally we rely on past experiences to determine the dimensional value of a quantity. For example, a rectangular board 3 ft. long and 2 ft. wide would contain an area of $3 \times 2 = 6$ sq. ft. By the proper use of dimensions it can be shown that the above answer must represent square feet. If the dimen-

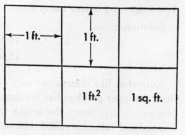

Fig. 5.1. Graphical representation of 6 ft.²

sional values of the quantities are treated in the same manner as the numerical values, then the resultant dimensional value must be the correct one. Thus, the rectangular board referred to above, and shown in Fig. 5.1, would have an area of:

$$2 \text{ ft.} \times 3 \text{ ft.} = (2 \times 3)(\text{ft.} \times \text{ft.}) = 6 \text{ ft.}^2$$

The dimensions ft.² may be read "feet squared" or "square feet."

25

Some Practical Applications of Dimensions

5.2. The Treatment of Dimensions in the Solution of Problems. Only quantities expressed in similar dimensions may be added or subtracted. Obviously there would be no significance to the sum obtained by adding quantities such as 15 in. and 27 cm. unless they were first converted to similar units. Quantities expressed either in like or unlike units may be multiplied and divided. It should also be remembered that in order to have a true equality, each side of the expression must be identical, both numerically and dimensionally. For example, in the expression 2 ft. $\times$ 3 ft. = 6 ft.^{2}, each side is equal numerically to 6 and dimensionally to ft.^{2}

Example 5.1. A man traveled 125 miles in 5 hours. What was his speed in miles per hour $\left(\dfrac{\text{mi.}}{\text{hr.}}\right)$?

Solution.

$$\frac{125 \text{ mi.}}{5 \text{ hr.}} = 25 \frac{\text{mi.}}{\text{hr.}}$$

Note that unlike dimensions such as mi. and hr. cannot be canceled and are therefore carried along as the dimensional value of the answer with the numerical value.

Example 5.2. Two iron rods are 75 ft. and 15 ft. respectively in length. The longer rod is how many times the length of the shorter rod?

Solution.

$$\frac{75 \text{ ft.}}{15 \text{ ft.}} = 5.$$

Note that like dimensions may be canceled. As a result the answer in this particular problem has no dimension. It merely indicates that one of two rods is five times the length of the other. Numbers which have no dimensional value are called pure or abstract numbers and occur frequently in mathematical operations.

Example 5.3. Convert 16 in. to cm.

Solution. There are 2.54 $\dfrac{\text{cm.}}{\text{in.}}$. Therefore, in 16 in. there would be:

$$16 \text{ in.} \times 2.54 \frac{\text{cm.}}{\text{in.}} = 40.6 \text{ cm.}$$

Example 5.4. A given solution of acid weighs 1.5 $\dfrac{\text{g.}}{\text{ml.}}$. Calculate the weight of 30 ml. of the acid.

Solution. The answer must have the dimensions grams. A simple mental calculation will show that $\cancel{ml.} \times \frac{g.}{\cancel{ml.}} = g.$ Therefore:

$$30 \; \cancel{ml.} \times 1.5 \; \frac{g.}{\cancel{ml.}} = 45 \; g.$$

Example 5.5. A solution of sulfuric acid weighs $1.84 \; \frac{g.}{ml.}$. How many milliliters of the acid would be required to weigh 86 g.?

Solution. Solving dimensionally we see that:

$$g. \div \frac{g.}{ml.} = \cancel{g.} \times \frac{ml.}{\cancel{g.}} = ml., \quad \text{and} \quad g. \times \frac{g.}{ml.} = g.^2 \; ml.$$

Evidently the first solution is the correct one since it gives the desired dimensions of volume. That is:

$$86 \; g. \div 1.84 \; \frac{g.}{ml.} = \left(\frac{86}{1.84} \right) \left(\cancel{g.} \times \frac{ml.}{\cancel{g.}} \right) = 47 \; ml.$$

Dimensional quantities are often separated from the numerical values as shown above in order to simplify the solution and evaluate the dimensions. Such treatment will give added significance to the solution.

Problems

5.1. Evaluate the following numerically and dimensionally:

a. $18 \; ft.^2 \div 3 \; ft.$

b. $13 \; \frac{g.}{cm.^3} \times 225 \; cm.^3$

c. $3 \; m.^2 \div 65 \; cm.$

d. $784 \; g. \div 4.00 \; \frac{g.}{cm.^3}$

e. $3.4 \; kg. \div 9.6 \; \frac{g.}{cm.^3}$

f. $(6 \; ft. \times 4 \; ft.) \div 3 \; ft.$

5.2. How many kilograms are there in 15 pounds?   *Ans.* 6.8 kg.

5.3. How many pounds are there in 15 kilograms?   *Ans.* 33 lb.

5.4. How many kilometers are there in 25 miles?   *Ans.* 40.2 km.

5.5. How many miles are there in 25 kilometers?   *Ans.* 15.5 mi.

5.6. A solution of hydrochloric acid weighs $1.12 \; \frac{g.}{ml.}$. Calculate:

a. The weight of 750 ml. of the solution.   *Ans.* 840 g.

b. The volume occupied by 750 g. of the solution.   *Ans.* 670 ml.

5.7. An experiment calls for 250 grams of concentrated sulfuric acid weighing $1.84 \; \frac{g.}{ml.}$. How many milliliters of the acid would be required?   *Ans.* 136 ml.

5.8. How many grams of glycerine, weighing 1.25 grams per milliliter, will a 125 ml. flask hold?   *Ans.* 156 g.

5.9. If 300 ml. of ether weighs 217.5 g., calculate its weight in grams per milliliter.   *Ans.* $0.725 \frac{g.}{ml.}$.

5.10. Calculate the milliliters per gram of the ether in problem 5.9, and of the glycerine in problem 5.8.   *Ans.* $1.38 \frac{ml.}{g.}$; $0.800 \frac{ml.}{g.}$.

6

The Densities of Substances

Density and specific gravity are two important physical concepts. Many of the fundamental principles presented in the previous chapters are used when solving problems involving these two concepts. The masses of substances given in problems in succeeding chapters will often be expressed in terms of density and volume.

The Amount of Matter in Substances

6.1. Density. Density is defined as the weight of a unit volume of a substance, where any unit of weight and any unit of volume may be used. In the metric system the gram and the cubic centimeter are commonly used as the units of weight and volume respectively. In the English system the pound and cubic foot are commonly used to express density. For example, the density of silver is $10.5 \frac{\text{g.}}{\text{cm.}^3}$, or $655 \frac{\text{lb.}}{\text{ft.}^3}$. Since the numerical value of the density of a substance depends upon the units of weight and volume chosen, it is essential that the dimensions be given when expressing density.

6.2. Specific Gravity. Specific gravity is defined as that number which indicates how many times heavier a substance is than an equal volume of a substance taken as a standard. Gases are usually referred to air as a standard; solids and liquids are referred to water. That is, volume for volume, silver is 10.5 times heavier than an equal volume of water.

Specific gravities may be calculated from densities. For example:

$$\text{Sp. gr. of iron} = \frac{\text{wt. of 1 cm.}^3 \text{ of iron}}{\text{wt. of 1 cm.}^3 \text{ of water}} = \frac{7.9 \frac{\text{g.}}{\text{cm.}^3}}{1.0 \frac{\text{g.}}{\text{cm.}^3}} = 7.9, \quad \text{or}$$

$$\text{Sp. gr. of iron} = \frac{\text{wt. of 1 ft.}^3 \text{ of iron}}{\text{wt. of 1 ft.}^3 \text{ of water}} = \frac{493 \frac{lb.}{ft.^3}}{62.4 \frac{lb.}{ft.^3}} = 7.9.$$

Several important facts are illustrated in the above calculations. First, specific gravity has no dimensions, since in each of the above calculations it will be observed that the dimensions cancel. Second, the specific gravity of a substance is independent of the units used. Third, a given volume of iron is 7.9 times as heavy as an equal volume of water. Fourth, the density and specific gravity of a substance are numerically the same when referred to water, and expressed as grams per cubic centimeter. This is because water weighs 1.00 gram per cubic centimeter. Fifth, specific gravity is a number which indicates how many times heavier a given volume of a substance is than an equal volume of water, if the substance is a solid or liquid; or than an equal volume of air, if the substance is a gas.

Some Practical Applications

6.3. Problems Involving Density and Specific Gravity.

Example 6.1. The specific gravity of silver is 10.5. What is the weight of a block of silver 2.5 cm. by 8.0 cm. by 4.0 cm.?

Solution. Volume for volume, silver is 10.5 times as heavy as water. Since water weighs 1.00 $\frac{g.}{cm.^3}$, then silver must weigh 10.5 $\frac{g.}{cm.^3}$. The next step therefore would be to find the volume of the block of silver in cubic centimeters. Then:

$$2.5 \text{ cm.} \times 8.0 \text{ cm.} \times 4.0 \text{ cm.} = 80 \text{ cm.}^3$$

and
$$80 \text{ cm.}^3 \times 10.5 \frac{g.}{cm.^3} = 840 \text{ g.}$$

Example 6.2. A solution of hydrochloric acid has a density of 1.2 $\frac{g.}{cm.^3}$ and is 35 per cent HCl by weight. How many grams of HCl would there be in 250 ml. of the acid solution?

Solution. Since the solution is 35 per cent HCl by weight, the first step would be to find the weight of 250 ml. of the solution.

$$250 \text{ ml.} \times 1.2 \frac{g.}{ml.} = 300 \text{ g.}$$

Then
$$300 \text{ g.} \times 0.35 = 105 \text{ g. of HCl.}$$

Example 6.3. A concentrated solution of sulfuric acid has a density of

1.84 $\frac{g.}{ml.}$ and is 95 per cent acid by weight. What volume of the solution would be required in order to obtain 360 grams of acid?

Solution. Since the given solution weighs 1.84 $\frac{g.}{ml.}$ and is 95 per cent acid by weight, then the solution would contain:

$$0.95 \times 1.84 \frac{g.}{ml.} = 1.75 \frac{g.}{ml.} \text{ of acid,}$$

and the volume of solution required to contain 360 g. of acid would be:

$$360 \text{ g.} \div 1.75 \frac{g.}{ml.} = \frac{360 \text{ g.}}{1.75 \frac{g.}{ml.}} = 206 \text{ ml.}$$

Problems

6.1. Calculate the weight of a block of metal 3.6 cm. by 4.5 cm. by 8.4 cm., the specific gravity of the metal being 8.45.   *Ans.* 1.1 × 10³ g.

6.2. Calculate the density of a liquid 17.45 ml. of which weighs 16.3 g.

$$Ans. \ 0.934 \frac{g.}{ml.}.$$

6.3. The density of a given block of stone is 368 pounds per cubic foot. Calculate its specific gravity.   *Ans.* 5.90.

6.4. The specific gravity of mercury is 13.6. Calculate the density of mercury in both English and metric units.

6.5. A cubic foot of iron weighs 428 pounds. Calculate the density of iron in ounces per cubic inch. $Ans. \ 3.96 \frac{oz.}{in.^3}.$

6.6. Calculate the density of cork if a cube measuring 1.5 cm. on a side weighs 1.00 g. $Ans. \ 0.30 \frac{g.}{cm.^3}.$

6.7. A bottle weighs 13.45 g. when empty and 16.72 g. when filled with water. The same bottle when filled with a solution of sulfuric acid weighs 19.01 g. Calculate the density of the acid solution.

$$Ans. \ 1.70 \frac{g.}{ml.}.$$

6.8. A carboy contains 41.3 kg. of hydrochloric acid, density 1.18 grams per milliliter. Calculate the volume of the carboy in liters.   *Ans.* 35.0 l.

6.9. Concentrated sulfuric acid has a density of 1.84 g. per ml. Calculate:
a. The weight of one liter of the acid.   *Ans.* 1840 g.
b. The amount of acid in one liter of solution if it contains 95 per cent acid by weight.   *Ans.* 1748 g.
c. The volume of acid solution required to contain 84 g. of sulfuric acid.   *Ans.* 48 ml.

6.10. What volume of lead, specific gravity 11.4, would be equal in weight to 100 ml. of sulfuric acid, density 1.84 g. per ml.?   *Ans.* 16.1 cm.³

7

Some Quantitative Relationships Involving the Gaseous State

Under suitable conditions most substances may exist either as a gas, liquid, or solid. Many chemical reactions occur involving substances in the gaseous state, both as reactants and products. It is important, therefore, that the physical laws relating to the gaseous state be understood before discussing problems involving chemical changes of substances existing in the gaseous state. Such physical laws relating to gases may usually be explained in terms of the kinetic energy of molecules.

The Energy of Molecules in the Gaseous State

7.1. The Kinetic-Molecular Theory of Matter. The principal difference between substances in the solid, liquid, and gaseous states lies in the freedom of movement of their molecules. The kinetic-molecular theory of matter deals with the energy associated with molecules due to their motion, the word *kinetic* coming from a Greek word meaning *motion*. Molecules in the liquid and solid states have a somewhat limited freedom of movement, whereas those in the gaseous state are limited in movement only by the walls of the containing vessel.

The kinetic energy of a particle in motion, whether it be a molecule or an aggregate of molecules, is given by the expression:

Kinetic energy in ergs = $\frac{1}{2}$ mv.^{2}

velocity in cm. per sec.

mass in grams

Since 10^7 ergs = 0.24 cal., then the above expression becomes:

Kinetic energy in calories = (1.2×10^{-8})mv.^{2}

32

The kinetic energy of all molecules is the same at any given temperature. This means that light molecules, such as hydrogen, must be moving at a greater velocity at any given temperature than are heavier molecules, such as oxygen, in order to compensate for the difference in mass.

7.2. The Pressure Exerted by Gaseous Molecules. Gases are composed of molecules which are vibrating in all directions within the container, as shown in Fig. 7.1.

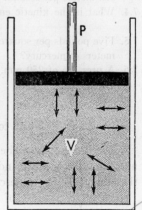

Gas pressure is the result of the impacts of the molecules on the walls of the containing vessel. The pressure exerted by the gas may be determined by measuring the force necessary to hold the piston, P, in a given position in the cylinder.

Pressure is defined as the *force* acting on a *unit surface area*, and may be expressed in any one of several conventional units. Steam pressure is usually measured in pounds per square inch. In scientific work a unit called the *atmosphere* is commonly used.

Fig. 7.1.   Pressure is produced by the impact of molecules on the walls of the containing vessel.

One atmosphere is the pressure exerted by the air on a unit surface area at sea level and is equal to:

1033 grams per square centimeter

or   14.7 pounds per square inch.

The equivalent of one atmosphere pressure is commonly used in the solution of problems involving gases, and should not be confused with the above absolute values. Considering equal cross-sectional areas, one atmosphere is equivalent to the pressure exerted by:

760 millimeters of mercury,

29.9 inches of mercury,

or   33.9 feet of water.

In the solution of problems involving gas pressure, any of the above absolute or equivalent values may be used, provided the same units are used consistently throughout the problem.

Problems

7.1. How would the kinetic energies of two bullets traveling at the same velocity compare if one bullet were twice the weight of the other?

7.2. How would the kinetic energies of two bullets of the same mass compare if one bullet were traveling at twice the velocity of the other?

7.3. What is the kinetic energy in ergs of a 12 gram bullet traveling at 350 meters per second? *Ans.* 7.35×10^9 ergs.

7.4. What is the kinetic energy in calories of the bullet in problem 7.3? *Ans.* 176 cal.

7.5. Five pounds per square inch would be equivalent to how many millimeters of mercury? *Ans.* 260 mm. of Hg.

7.6. A pressure of 250 mm. of Hg. would be equivalent to how many atmospheres? *Ans.* 0.329 atm.

Laws Relating to Molecules in the Gaseous State

7.3. Introduction. The volume of a given mass of gas is dependent upon the temperature and pressure under which the gas exists. It is, therefore, possible to describe the physical behavior of gases in terms

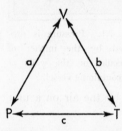

Fig. 7.2. Relationship among the variables pressure, temperature, and volume, for substances in the gaseous state: (a) law of Boyle; (b) law of Charles; (c) law of Gay-Lussac.

of the three variables: *temperature*, T; *pressure*, P; and *volume*, V. For a given volume of gas under given conditions of temperature and pressure, a change in any one or more of the three variables will result in a change in the remaining variables according to definitely established laws called the *gas laws*. As shown in Fig. 7.2, the relationship between any two of the variables may be studied, provided the remaining variable is maintained constant.

7.4. The Law of Charles. The law of Charles expresses the relationship between the two variables, temperature and volume, for a given mass of gas, the pressure remaining constant. The pressure must remain constant in order that the observed change in volume may be attributed solely to the change in temperature. The relationship is expressed in the law of Charles: pressure constant, the volume of a given mass of gas varies *directly* with the *absolute temperature*. That is:

$$V \propto T \text{ (pressure and mass of gas constant).}$$

The above proportionality indicates that although V and T may not be equal numerically, they vary proportionately with each other. This is shown in Table 7.1.

TABLE 7.1

THE VARIATION IN THE VOLUME OF A GIVEN MASS OF GAS WITH
TEMPERATURE, PRESSURE CONSTANT

Temperature (T)	Volume (V)
274° K.	500 ml.
548° K.	1000 ml.
137° K.	250 ml.

From Table 7.1 we see that:

$$\frac{V}{T} = \frac{500 \text{ ml.}}{274° \text{ K.}} = \frac{1000 \text{ ml.}}{548° \text{ K.}} = \frac{250 \text{ ml.}}{137° \text{ K.}} = 1.82.$$

That is, for a given mass of gas at constant pressure:

$$\frac{V}{T} = K, \quad \text{and} \quad \frac{V'}{T'} = K, \text{ where K is a constant.}$$

Things equal to the same thing are equal to each other. Therefore:

$$\frac{V}{T} = \frac{V'}{T'}$$

or

$$V' = V \times \frac{T'}{T}.$$

temperature correction fraction

original volume at T

corrected volume at T'

Example 7.1. A cylinder contained 600 ml. of air at 20° C. What would be the volume of the air at 40° C., pressure constant?

Solution. The four quantities involved are:

Original conditions: V = 600 ml.
T = 20 + 273 = 293° K.

Corrected conditions: V' = x ml.
T' = 40 + 273 = 313° K.

The 600 ml. volume will increase proportionately with the temperature. The temperature correction fraction must, therefore, be greater than unity.

That is, $\frac{T'}{T} = \frac{313° \text{ K.}}{293° \text{ K.}}$. Then:

$$V' = 600 \text{ ml.} \times \frac{313° \text{ K.}}{293° \text{ K.}}$$

$$= 641 \text{ ml.}$$

7.5. The Law of Boyle. The law of Boyle deals with the relationship existing between the two variables, pressure and volume, for a given mass of gas at constant temperature. The relationship is expressed in the law of Boyle: temperature constant, the volume of a given mass of gas varies *inversely* with the *pressure*. That is:

$$V \propto \frac{1}{P} \text{ (temperature and mass of gas constant).}$$

The variation of volume with pressure, as expressed in the law of Boyle, is shown in Table 7.2.

TABLE 7.2

THE VARIATION IN THE VOLUME OF A GIVEN MASS OF GAS WITH
PRESSURE, TEMPERATURE CONSTANT

Pressure (P)	Volume (V)
760 mm. of Hg	500 ml.
1520 mm. of Hg	250 ml.
380 mm. of Hg	1000 ml.

From Table 7.2 we see that:

$$PV = (760)(500) = (1520)(250) = (380)(1000) = 380,000.$$

That is, for a given mass of gas at constant temperature:

$$PV = K, \text{ and } P'V' = K, \text{ where K is a constant.}$$

Since things equal to the same thing are equal to each other, then:

$$PV = P'V'$$

or
$$V' = V \times \frac{P}{P'}.$$

    pressure correction fraction
   original volume at P
corrected volume at P'

Example 7.2. A volume of air measuring 380 ml. was collected at a pressure of 640 mm. of Hg. Calculate the volume the air would occupy at a pressure of 760 mm. of Hg, temperature constant.

Solution. The four quantities involved are:

Original conditions: V = 380 ml.

                P = 640 mm. of Hg.

Corrected conditions: V' = x ml.

                 P' = 760 mm. of Hg.

Since the pressure increases, the volume will decrease. This means that the pressure correction fraction is less than unity. That is:

$$\frac{P}{P'} = \frac{640 \text{ mm. of Hg}}{760 \text{ mm. of Hg}}.$$

Then

$$V' = 380 \text{ ml.} \times \frac{640 \text{ ~~mm. of Hg~~}}{760 \text{ ~~mm. of Hg~~}}$$

$$= 320 \text{ ml.}$$

7.6. The Law of Gay-Lussac. The law of Gay-Lussac deals with the relationship existing between the two variables, pressure and temperature, for a given mass of gas at constant volume. The relationship is expressed in the law of Gay-Lussac: volume constant, the pressure exerted by a given mass of gas varies *directly* with the *absolute temperature*. That is:

$$P \propto T \text{ (volume and mass of gas constant).}$$

It will be observed that the same type of variation exists between pressure and temperature as exists between volume and temperature (Sec. 7.4). Then:

$$\frac{P}{T} = \frac{P'}{T'}$$

or

$$P' = P \times \frac{T'}{T}.$$

temperature correction fraction

original pressure at T

corrected pressure at T'

Example 7.3. The air in a tank was at a pressure of 640 mm. of Hg at 23° C. When placed in sunlight the temperature rose to 48° C. What was the pressure in the tank?

Solution. A rise in temperature would result in a rise in pressure. Therefore, the temperature correction fraction must be greater than unity. That is:

$$P' = 640 \text{ mm. of Hg} \times \frac{(273 + 48)° \text{ ~~K.~~}}{(273 + 23)° \text{ ~~K.~~}}$$

$$= 694 \text{ mm. of Hg.}$$

7.7. A General Gas Law. A general gas law would involve the three variables, temperature, pressure, and volume, simultaneously. Such a general gas law may be obtained by combining any two of the three gas laws discussed previously, since the three variables would be involved. For example, consider the laws of Charles and Boyle combined to give one equation.

$$V \propto T, \quad \text{and} \quad V \propto \frac{1}{P}.$$

Then $\qquad V \propto \frac{T}{P}, \quad \text{or} \quad V = K\frac{T}{P}, \quad \text{and} \quad K = \frac{PV}{T}.$

For a second set of conditions V', T', and P':

$$K = \frac{P'V'}{T'}.$$

Therefore, $\quad \dfrac{PV}{T} = \dfrac{P'V'}{T'}$ (for a given mass of gas)

and $\qquad V' = V \times \dfrac{T'}{T} \times \dfrac{P}{P'}.$

pressure correction fraction

temperature correction fraction

original volume at T and P

corrected volume at T' and P'

Example 7.4. A volume of 250 ml. of oxygen was collected at 20° C. and 785 mm. of Hg. The next day the temperature was 37° C. and the pressure 770 mm. of Hg. Calculate the resultant volume of the oxygen.

Solution. The quantities involved are:

Original conditions: P = 785 mm. of Hg.
$\qquad\qquad\qquad\quad$ V = 250 ml.
$\qquad\qquad\qquad\quad$ T = 293° K.

Corrected conditions: P' = 770 mm. of Hg.
$\qquad\qquad\qquad\quad\;$ V' = x ml.
$\qquad\qquad\qquad\quad\;$ T' = 310° K.

Both the increase in temperature and the decrease in pressure will result in an increase in volume of the oxygen. Therefore:

$$V' = 250 \text{ ml.} \times \frac{310° \text{K.}}{293° \text{K.}} \times \frac{785 \text{ mm. of Hg}}{770 \text{ mm. of Hg}}$$

$$= 270 \text{ ml.}$$

7.8. The Change in Density of a Gas with Changes in Temperature and Pressure. Since the volume of a given mass of gas is dependent upon the temperature and pressure under which it exists, it is apparent that the density of a gas will be dependent upon these same variables.

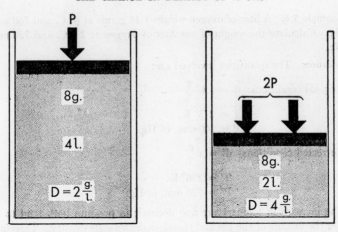

Fig. 7.3. Variation in the density of a gas with pressure.

From Fig. 7.3 we see that the density of a gas varies *directly* with the *pressure;* from Fig. 7.4 we see that the density varies *inversely* with the *absolute temperature.* That is:

$$d \propto P, \quad \text{and} \quad d \propto \frac{1}{T}.$$

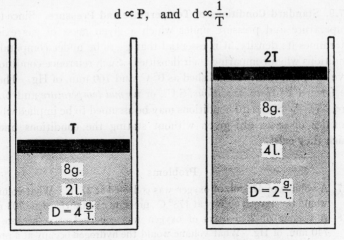

Fig. 7.4. Variation in the density of a gas with temperature.

Developing the above two relationships in the same manner as the variables in Sec. 7.4 and Sec. 7.5 we have:

$$\frac{dT}{P} = \frac{d'T'}{P'} \quad \text{(for a given mass of gas)}$$

or

$$d' = d \times \frac{T}{T'} \times \frac{P'}{P}.$$

Example 7.5. A liter of oxygen weighs 1.43 grams at 0° C. and 760 mm. of Hg. Calculate the weight of one liter of oxygen at 23° C. and 720 mm. of Hg.

Solution. The quantities involved are:

Original conditions: d = 1.43 $\frac{g.}{l.}$

$$T = 273° K.$$
$$P = 760 \text{ mm. of Hg.}$$

Corrected conditions: d' = $x \frac{g.}{l.}$

$$T' = 296° K.$$
$$P' = 720 \text{ mm. of Hg.}$$

The increase in temperature and decrease in pressure both tend to increase the volume of the gas and therefore decrease its density. Therefore:

$$d' = 1.43 \frac{g.}{l.} \times \frac{273° \cancel{K.}}{296° \cancel{K.}} \times \frac{720 \cancel{\text{ mm. of Hg}}}{760 \cancel{\text{ mm. of Hg}}}$$

$$= 1.25 \frac{g.}{l.}.$$

7.9. Standard Conditions of Temperature and Pressure. Since the temperature and pressure under which a given mass of gas exists determines its density, it is essential that gases be under comparable conditions when comparing their densities. Such reference conditions have been arbitrarily established as 0° C. and 760 mm. of Hg. These are termed *standard conditions*, S.C., or *normal temperature* and *pressure*, N.T.P. Standard conditions may be assumed to be implied when densities of gases are given without stating the conditions under which they exist.

Problems

7.7. A volume of 473 ml. of oxygen was collected at 27° C. What volume would the oxygen occupy at 173° C., pressure constant? *Ans.* 703 ml.

7.8. A volume of 2.45 liters of oxygen was collected at a pressure of 740 mm. of Hg. What volume would the hydrogen occupy at a pressure of 765 mm. of Hg? *Ans.* 2.37 l.

7.9. A balloon required 32,500 cubic feet of helium to fill it at 86° F. and one atmosphere pressure. Would the helium expand or contract and how much if the balloon ascended to a point where the temperature was 14° F. and the pressure one-half an atmosphere? *Ans.* 23,900 ft.[3]

7.10. The pressure on a cubic foot of air was increased from 14.7 pounds per square inch to 231 pounds per square inch, temperature constant. Calculate the volume of the air. *Ans.* 0.064 ft.[3].

7.11. A volume of 21.5 ml. of oxygen was collected in a tube over mercury at a temperature of 17° C. and 740 mm. of Hg. The next day the volume of oxygen was observed to be 22.1 ml. with the barometer still at 740 mm. of Hg. What was the temperature of the laboratory? *Ans.* 25° C.

7.12. A room is 16 ft. by 12 ft. by 12 ft. Would air enter or leave the room and how much if the temperature changed from 27° C. to −3° C., pressure remaining constant? *Ans.* 231 ft.³

7.13. A volume of 84 ml. of a gas was collected at standard conditions. At what pressure would the volume be 100 ml., temperature constant? *Ans.* 638 mm. of Hg.

7.14. A bottle of nitrogen was collected at 0° C. Assuming the pressure to remain constant, at what temperature would the volume be doubled? *Ans.* 273° C.

7.15. An automobile tire contains air at 38 lb. per in.² How many times the original volume would the air in the tire occupy if released at 15 lb. per in.², temperature constant? Note: a tire gauge registers excess over atmospheric pressure. *Ans.* 3.5 times.

7.16. The temperature of a tire rose from 50° F. to 120° F. as the result of traveling on a hot pavement. Assuming the volume of the tire to be constant, what was the resulting pressure in the tire if the initial pressure was 40 lb. per in.²? *Ans.* 46 $\frac{\text{lb.}}{\text{in.}^2}$.

7.17. A gas occupies a volume of 50 ml. at 30° C. and 680 mm. of Hg. Calculate the volume the gas would occupy at standard conditions. *Ans.* 40 ml.

7.18. A volume of 385 ml. of air at 760 mm. of Hg and 27° C. was carried to a mountain top where the temperature was −23° C. and the pressure 470 mm. of Hg. Calculate the resultant volume of the air. *Ans.* 519 ml.

7.19. At the place Piccard started his ascent in the stratosphere balloon, the temperature was 17° C. and the pressure 640 mm. of Hg. At the highest altitude reached, the temperature was −48° C. and the pressure 310 mm. of Hg. To what fractional part of its total capacity was the balloon filled before ascending in order that it would be fully expanded at the highest altitude reached? *Ans.* 0.63.

7.20. A given quantity of gas occupies a volume of 875 ml. at 68° F. and 73 cm. of Hg. Calculate the volume the gas would occupy at 350° K. and 12 atmospheres pressure. *Ans.* 84 ml.

7.21. A tank containing 4 ft.³ of butane gas at 15 atm. pressure is connected to a tank containing 6 ft.³ of the gas at 5 atm. pressure. Calculate the resultant pressure in the connected tanks, assuming no temperature change. *Ans.* 9 atm.

7.22. Air weighs 1.29 grams per liter at S.C. Calculate the density of the air on Pikes Peak when the pressure is 450 mm. of Hg and the temperature 17° C. *Ans.* 0.719 $\frac{g.}{l.}$.

7.23. One liter of nitrogen weighs 1.25 grams at S.C. At what temperature would the density be one-half this value, pressure constant?
Ans. 273° C.

7.24. One liter of a gas weighs 1.33 grams at 750 mm. of Hg and 17° C. Calculate the weight of 500 ml. of the gas at 640 mm. of Hg and 37° C. *Ans.* 0.53 g.

7.25. An automobile tire gauge registered 40 lb. with the barometer reading 760 mm. of Hg and the temperature 23° C. After driving on a hot pavement the gauge registered 43 lb. What was the temperature of the tire, assuming its volume to remain constant? *Ans.* 39° C.

7.26. A closed metal cylinder contains air at a pressure of 930 mm. of Hg and a temperature of 27° C. To what temperature would the air in the cylinder have to be raised in order to exert a pressure of 1500 mm. of Hg? *Ans.* 211° C·

Laws Relating to Mixtures of Gases

7.10. Dalton's Law of Partial Pressures. Dalton's law states that the total pressure exerted by a mixture of gases is equal to the sum of the partial pressures of each of the gases constituting the mixture. By *partial pressure* is meant the pressure each gas would exert if it alone occupied the volume occupied by the mixture of gases. For example, if one liter of hydrogen and one liter of oxygen, each at 0° C. and 380 mm. of Hg, are forced into a third container of one liter capacity as shown in Fig. 7.5, then the resultant pressure of the mixture would be:

380 mm. of Hg + 380 mm. of Hg = 760 mm. of Hg.

total pressure

partial pressure of oxygen

partial pressure of hydrogen

Dalton's law finds its most useful application in general chemistry to calculations involving the collection of gases over water, where water vapor is always present with the collected gas. In such calculations a correction must be made for the water vapor present. The higher the temperature of the water over which the gas is collected, the greater the amount of water vapor present. The actual amount of gas collected is therefore less than the measured volume. In Fig. 7.6 the gas, G, has been collected over the water, L. The space

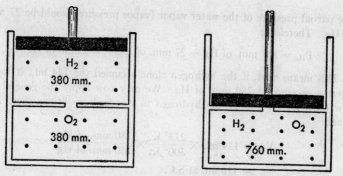

Fig. 7.5. Illustrating Dalton's law of partial pressures.

G therefore contains both water vapor and gas. If the level of the liquid is the same inside and outside the tube, T, then the pressure of the gases in the tube is equal to the barometric pressure of the room in which the gas is collected. Then, from Dalton's law:

$$P_g + P_w = P_a.$$

atmospheric pressure
partial pressure of water vapor
partial pressure of the collected gas

Solving the above for P_g gives:

$$P_g = P_a - P_w.$$

Therefore, to find the pressure, P_g, under which the collected gas would exist if it alone occupied the total volume in the tube, subtract the vapor pressure of the water at the given temperature from the atmospheric pressure. A table giving the vapor pressure of water for temperatures ranging from 0° C. to 100° C. will be found in the appendix.

Example 7.6. Hydrogen was collected over water at 27° C. and 807 mm. of Hg. The volume of gas above the water was 124 ml. Calculate the volume the hydrogen would occupy dry at S.C.

Solution. First calculate the partial pressure of the hydrogen. At 27° C.

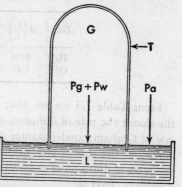

Fig. 7.6. Dalton's law of partial pressures applied to gases collected over water.

the partial pressure of the water vapor (vapor pressure) would be 27 mm. of Hg. Therefore:

$$P_{H_2} = 807 \text{ mm. of Hg} - 27 \text{ mm. of Hg} = 780 \text{ mm. of Hg.}$$

This means that, if the hydrogen alone occupied the 124 ml., it would exert a pressure of 780 mm. of Hg. We may now apply the general gas law (Sec. 7.7) to change the hydrogen to standard conditions (Sec. 7.9). Then:

$$V_{H_2} = 124 \text{ ml.} \times \frac{273° \cancel{K.}}{300° \cancel{K.}} \times \frac{780 \cancel{\text{ mm. of Hg}}}{760 \cancel{\text{ mm. of Hg}}}$$

$$= 116 \text{ ml. at S.C.}$$

7.11. Graham's Law of Gaseous Diffusion. The law of Graham deals with the relationship existing between the *rates of diffusion*, D, of gases, and their *densities*, d. By diffusion is meant the ability of gaseous molecules to pass through small openings, such as in the fabric of balloons or unglazed porcelain; or the intermingling of molecules in a mixture. On the basis of the kinetic-molecular theory it is evident that increasing the temperature of a gas will increase its rate of diffusion, since increasing the temperature increases the velocity of the molecules, thus producing a greater number of impacts on the walls of the containing vessel in any given unit of time. It is also apparent that increasing the pressure of a gas will produce more impacts on the walls of the vessel, thus increasing the rate of diffusion.

TABLE 7.3

DIFFUSION OF GASES AS RELATED TO THEIR DENSITIES

Gas	$d \left(\frac{g.}{l.} \right)$	$\sqrt{d}$	$D \left(\frac{ml.}{hr.} \right)$
H_2	0.09	0.3	400
O_2	1.43	1.2	100

From Table 7.3 we see that the greater the density of the gas, the slower the rate of diffusion of the gas. This is in accord with the law of Graham: under similar conditions such as temperature, pressure, and the size of the openings through which the gases diffuse, the rates of diffusion of gases vary *inversely* as the *square roots* of their *densities*. That is:

$$D \propto \frac{1}{\sqrt{d}}.$$

Treating the above variables in the same manner as the variables pressure and volume in Sec. 7.5, we have:

$$D\sqrt{d} = D'\sqrt{d'}$$

or
$$D' = D \times \frac{\sqrt{d}}{\sqrt{d'}} = D \times \sqrt{\frac{d}{d'}}.$$

When one considers that light molecules are moving with a greater velocity than are heavier molecules (Sec. 7.1), it becomes evident why the lighter molecules will diffuse the faster.

Example 7.7. Two balloons of the same size and like material are filled respectively with hydrogen and oxygen at the same temperature and pressure. If the oxygen escapes at the rate of 65 ml. per hour, calculate the rate of escape of the hydrogen.

Solution. Using the values of the densities given in Table 7.3, we have:

$$D_{H_2} = 65 \frac{ml.}{hr.} \times \sqrt{\frac{1.43}{0.09}}$$

$$= 260 \frac{ml.}{hr.}.$$

Since the hydrogen is the lighter of the two gases it will diffuse the faster. Also, the quantity $\sqrt{\frac{1.43}{0.09}} = 4$ tells us that hydrogen will diffuse four times faster than oxygen.

The densities of gases are proportional to their molecular weights. For example in the case of oxygen and hydrogen, we have:

$$\frac{1.43 \frac{g.}{l.}}{0.09 \frac{g.}{l.}} = \frac{32.00}{2.016} = 15.9.$$

It is therefore possible to substitute the molecular weights of the gases, M, for their densities in the above formula. That is:

$$D' = D \times \sqrt{\frac{M}{M'}}.$$

Example 7.8. Compare the rates of diffusion of methane, CH_4, and sulfur dioxide, SO_2.

Solution. The molecular weight of $CH_4 = 16$ and of $SO_2 = 64$. Therefore the CH_4 will diffuse the faster. Let the rate of diffusion of SO_2 be unity. Then:

$$\text{Rate of diffusion of } CH_4 = 1 \times \sqrt{\tfrac{64}{16}} = 2.$$

That is, CH_4 diffuses twice as fast as SO_2.

Problems

7.27. Hydrogen was collected over water, the volume of hydrogen and water vapor being one liter at 25° C. and 640 mm. of Hg.

a. What is the partial pressure of the hydrogen? *Ans.* 616 mm. of Hg.

b. Calculate the volume the hydrogen would occupy dry under the given conditions. *Ans.* 0.963 l.

c. Calculate the volume the hydrogen would occupy dry at standard conditions. *Ans.* 0.742 l.

d. What fractional part of the original liter was water vapor?

Ans. 0.038.

7.28. In a laboratory experiment 763 ml. of gas was collected over water at 35° C. and 748 mm. of Hg. Calculate the volume the gas would occupy dry at standard conditions. *Ans.* 628 ml.

7.29. A volume of 1.43 liters of dry hydrogen at 27° C. and 760 mm. of Hg was bubbled through water. What was the volume of the mixture of hydrogen and water vapor, temperature and pressure constant? *Ans.* 1.48 l.

7.30. Nitrogen weighs 1.25 g. per l. and chlorine 3.21 g. per l. at standard conditions. Which will escape the faster and by how much if enclosed in an unglazed porcelain container in equal amounts?

Ans. N_2, 1.6 times faster.

7.31. Chlorine will escape through a small opening one-sixth as fast as hydrogen under similar conditions. Given that one liter of hydrogen weighs 0.0899 g., calculate the density of chlorine. *Ans.* 3.24 g. per l.

7.32. Three similar balloons were filled respectively with O_2, CO_2, and Cl_2 under similar conditions. In 10 hours one-half the CO_2 had escaped. How much of each of the other gases had escaped during this same period of time? *Ans.* $O_2 = 0.6$; $Cl_2 = 0.4$.

7.33. Two porous containers were filled respectively with hydrogen and oxygen at S.C. At the end of one hour 880 ml. of hydrogen had escaped. How much oxygen had escaped during this same period of time? *Ans.* 220 ml.

7.34. A porous container was filled with equal amounts of oxygen and a gas of unknown molecular weight. The oxygen escaped 1.77 times faster than the unknown gas. Calculate the molecular weight of the unknown gas. *Ans.* 99.

7.35. Prove that the densities of gases are proportional to their molecular weights.

7.36. Calculate the partial pressures of oxygen and nitrogen in the atmosphere, given that air contains 21 per cent oxygen and 78 per cent nitrogen by volume. Barometric pressure, 746 mm. of Hg.

Ans. $O_2 = 157$; $N_2 = 582$.

8

Chemical Units Involving Mass

The establishment of fundamental units is essential in order to solve problems. The chemist and physicist have devised certain fundamental units of mass based upon the actual masses of atoms and molecules. The student must be familiar with the meaning and usage of such units in order to solve problems in chemistry. Several of the more common units are defined and their use is explained.

Relative Units of Mass

8.1. Atomic and Formula Weights. An atom or molecule is too small to weigh, even on the most sensitive balance made. However, scientists are able to weigh masses containing a known number of atoms or molecules, thus making it possible to actually determine the weight of a single atom or molecule.

Since the weight in grams of an atom or molecule is extremely small, a system of relative weights, called *atomic weights*, has been devised. The atomic weights of the elements are based upon the oxygen atom as having a relative weight of 16.0000 units. For example, the atomic weight of sulfur is 32.066, which means that an atom of sulfur is $32.066 \div 16.000 = 2.004$ times heavier than an oxygen atom. An atom of uranium is $238.07 \div 16.00 = 14.88$ times heavier than an oxygen atom.

The atoms of the elements are the building stones of all substances, always combining in the same ratio under similar conditions to form the same substance. Since substances are made up of definite ratios of atoms, the sum of the weights of the atoms as designated in the formula represents the *formula weight* of that substance. Following are the formula weights of a number of substances:

Water, $H_2O = (2 \times 1.008) + 16.000 = 18.016$;

formula weight
contribution of oxygen atom
contribution of hydrogen atoms

47

Salt, NaCl = 22.997 + 35.457 = 58.454;

Sugar, $C_{12}H_{22}O_{11}$ = $(12 \times 12.01) + (22 \times 1.008) + (11 \times 16.00)$
$= 342.30$.

In the case of nonionic compounds such as water and sugar the formula weight represents a true molecular weight. However, with ionic compounds such as sodium chloride the formula merely represents the ratio of ions in the substance, there being no entity such as a molecule. The term molecular weight, therefore, has no significance in the case of ionic compounds.

Example 8.1. Calculate the formula weight of $Fe_2(SO_4)_3$.

Solution. The formula weight would be the sum of the weights of the atoms making up the formula. Therefore:

$$
\begin{array}{ll}
\text{iron contributes } 2 \times 55.85 & = 111.70 \text{ units} \\
\text{sulfur contributes } 3 \times 32.066 & = 96.20 \text{ units} \\
\text{oxygen contributes } 12 \times 16.00 & = \underline{192.00 \text{ units}} \\
\text{formula weight} & = 399.90 \text{ units.}
\end{array}
$$

Arbitrarily Established Chemical Units of Mass

8.2. The Gram-atom as a Chemical Unit of Mass. Even though the atomic weights of the elements are relative weights, they may be expressed in absolute weights such as grams, pounds, and tons. When expressed as grams, the formula weight becomes the *gram-atomic weight* or, for convenience, the *gram-atom*. For example, one gram-atom of oxygen would be 16.0000 grams, and two gram-atoms of sulfur would be $2 \times 32.066 = 64.132$ grams. Also, 32.066 pounds of sulfur would be one *pound-atom*.

Example 8.2. How many gram-atoms would there be in a bottle containing 1000 grams of mercury?

Solution. One gram-atom of mercury would be 200.61 grams. Therefore, 1000 grams of mercury would represent:

$$\frac{1000}{200.61} = 4.98 \text{ gram-atoms.}$$

8.3. The Mole as a Chemical Unit of Mass. Just as the atomic weight of an element may be expressed in grams to become the gram-atomic weight, so the formula weight of a substance may be designated in grams to become the *gram-molecular weight*, abbreviated *mole* for convenience. Similarly, we may have a *pound-molecular weight* or *ton-molecular weight*. Note that the quantity is called the gram-molecular weight whether it originates from the formula weight of ionic compounds or from the true molecular weight of nonionic compounds.

Example 8.3. How many grams of $Fe_2(SO_4)_3$ would there be in 2.75 moles of the compound?

Solution. From Example 8.1 we see that one mole of the compound would be equal to 399.90 grams. Therefore, 2.75 moles of $Fe_2(SO_4)_3$ would be:

$$2.75 \times 399.90 = 1100 \text{ g.}$$

Example 8.4. How many moles are there in one pound of sugar?

Solution. One pound is equal to 454 grams. Also, from Sec. 8.1 we see that one mole of sugar is equal to 342.30 grams. Therefore, 454 grams of sugar would be:

$$\frac{454}{342.30} = 1.33 \text{ moles.}$$

8.4. The Avogadro Number. Evidently there is some fundamental reason for the use of the gram-atom and the mole as chemical units of mass. The atomic weights of the elements are in the same ratio as the absolute weights of the atoms in grams. For example:

$$\frac{\text{weight of one atom of He}}{\text{weight of one atom of O}_2} = \frac{\text{atomic weight of He}}{\text{atomic weight of O}_2}$$

or

$$\frac{6.65 \times 10^{-24} \text{ g.}}{26.58 \times 10^{-24} \text{ g.}} = \frac{4.003}{16.000}.$$

It follows therefore that one gram-atom of each of the 98 elements contains the same number of atoms. For example, 16.0000 g. of oxygen contains the same number of atoms as 32.066 g. of sulfur. This number has been determined experimentally and found to be 6.023×10^{23} atoms per gram-atom. It is called the Avogadro number in honor of the Italian scientist Amedeo Avogadro (1776–1856). For convenience the number is commonly designated by the letter "N." Similarly, one mole of a substance contains N molecules of that substance.

Example 8.5. Show that one mole of water contains N molecules.

Solution. One mole of water contains:

$$
\begin{array}{ll}
2.00 \text{ gram-atoms of hydrogen} & = 2 \text{ N atoms} \\
1.00 \text{ gram-atom of oxygen} & = \underline{\text{ N atoms}} \\
\text{Therefore, 1.00 mole of } H_2O & = \overline{3 \text{ N atoms.}}
\end{array}
$$

However, there are 3 atoms per molecule of water.

Therefore,   1.00 mole of $H_2O = \dfrac{\cancel{N} \text{ atoms}}{\dfrac{\cancel{N}\text{ atoms}}{\text{molecule}}} = N$ molecules.

The one fact of basic importance to the scientist is that the gram-atom and the mole represent units of mass containing equal numbers of atoms and molecules — the fundamental units involved in chemical reactions.

Problems

8.1. How many atoms are represented by each of the following formulas: Fe_2O_3, $Fe(OH)_3$, $Ca(HCO_3)_2$, C_5H_{12}, $Na_2S_2O_7$, $Fe(C_2O_4)_3$, $(NH_4)_2Cr_2O_7$, $(NH_4)_2SO_4$, $Mg_3(PO_4)_2$, $C_6H_{12}O_6$, P_2O_5, Na_3PO_4?

8.2. What is the total number of atoms represented in each of the following expressions: $2\ Fe_2O_3$, $3\ Ca(HCO_3)_2$, $4\ Fe(OH)_3$, $5\ (NH_4)_2Cr_2O_7$, $6\ H_2$, $7\ Fe$, $8\ C_5H_{12}$, $9\ AlPO_4$, $10\ (NH_4)_2SO_4$?

8.3. What is the weight in grams of one atom of lead?

Ans. 344×10^{-24} g.

8.4. What is the weight in grams of 2 N atoms of aluminum?

Ans. 53.94 g.

8.5. Given that an atom of mercury weighs 333×10^{-24} g., calculate the atomic weight of mercury by means of N.   *Ans.* 200.6.

8.6. How many times heavier is an atom of silver than an atom of iron?

Ans. 1.93.

8.7. How many atoms are there in one cm.^{3} of lead, density 11.3 g. per cm.^{3}?   *Ans.* 3.28×10^{22}.

8.8. Determine the formula weight of each of the substances given in problem 8.1.

8.9. How many moles are there in each of the following?

a. 250 g. of SO_2.
b. 1.00 g. of SO_2.
c. 250 g. of Fe_2O_3.
d. 1.00 g. of Fe_2O_3.
e. 250 g. of O_2.
f. 1.00 g. of O_2.

Ans. a. 3.90; b. 0.0156; c. 4.27; d. 0.00626; e. 7.81; f. 0.0313.

8.10. How many millimoles are there in one mole?

8.11. How many millimoles are there in 1.00 g. of O_2?   *Ans.* 31.

8.12. How many grams are there in each of the following?

a. 2.65 moles of NaCl.
b. 1.50 moles of sulfur.
c. 0.75 mole of $C_{12}H_{22}O_{11}$.
d. 5.00 moles of nitrogen.

Ans. a. 155 g.; b. 48.099 g.; c. 257 g.; d. 140 g.

8.13. How many molecules are there in 0.75 mole of CO_2?   *Ans.* 0.75 N.

8.14. How many molecules are there in 0.75 mole of Fe?   *Ans.* 0.75 N.

8.15. How many atoms are there in 0.75 mole of oxygen?

Ans. 1.5 N atoms.

8.16. How many atoms are there in 0.75 mole of Fe?   *Ans.* 0.75 N.

8.17. What is the weight in grams of one molecule of water?

Ans. 30×10^{-24} g.

8.18. How many gram-atomic weights each of sodium and chlorine are there in one mole of sodium chloride? *Ans.* N each.

8.19. How many times heavier is a molecule of oxygen than a molecule of hydrogen? *Ans.* 15.9 times.

8.20. How many times heavier is an atom of oxygen than an atom of hydrogen? *Ans.* 15.9 times.

8.21. How many times heavier is an atom of oxygen than a molecule of hydrogen? *Ans.* 7.94.

8.22. How many times heavier is a molecule of CO_2 than a molecule of CH_4? *Ans.* 2.75 times.

8.23. How many grams are there in two gram-atoms of copper?

Ans. 127.08 g.

8.24. What is the weight in grams of 0.4 gram-atom of sulfur?

Ans. 12.8 g.

8.25. How many gram-atoms of iron are there in a cube of iron 4.00 cm. on a side, given that the density of iron is 7.9 g. per cm.^{3}? *Ans.* 9.1 g.-atoms.

8.26. What is the weight in grams of 10^{30} atoms of oxygen?

Ans. 2.66×10^7 g.

8.27. A mixture contains 0.25 gram-atom of iron and 1.25 gram-atoms of sulfur. What is the weight of the mixture? *Ans.* 54.1 g.

8.28. Prove that one mole of sugar, $C_{12}H_{22}O_{11}$, contains N molecules.

8.29. How many atoms of sulfur are there in 1.00 g. of sulfur?

Ans. 1.9×10^{22}.

8.30. How many atoms of oxygen would be required to weigh 8.00 g.?

Ans. 0.5 N atom.

8.31. How many moles are there in one liter of water? *Ans.* 55.5 moles.

8.32. An experiment calls for one-half mole of zinc. How many grams would be required? *Ans.* 32.69 g.

8.33. How many moles of H_2SO_4 would be contained in 250 ml. of a 95 per cent solution of sulfuric acid, density $1.84 \frac{g.}{ml.}$? *Ans.* 4.5 moles.

8.34. One liter of hydrogen chloride gas weighs 1.63 grams at standard conditions. How many liters are there in one mole of hydrogen chloride at standard conditions? *Ans.* 22.4 l.

8.35. How many grams are there in one pound-molecular weight of zinc sulfate, $ZnSO_4$? *Ans.* 7.3×10^4 g.

9

Combining Proportions among the Elements

The previous chapters have dealt with fundamentals which the student must understand in order to speak the language of the chemist. We are now ready to use some of these fundamental ideas in studying the mass relationships involved when the various elements combine to form compounds. In order for the chemist to explain quantitatively the laws controlling the formation of compounds from elements a unit of mass called the gram-equivalent weight has been devised. This represents the third unit of mass discussed based upon the actual masses of atoms and molecules, the gram-atom and mole having been presented in Chapter 8.

Relative Combining Proportions

9.1. Introduction. Under similar conditions, such as temperature and pressure, the atoms of two or more elements which react to form a compound will always combine in the same ratio. For example, when hydrogen burns in oxygen the product is H_2O, indicating that two atoms of hydrogen combine with one of oxygen. Also, excluding variations due to isotopes, the atoms of a given element all possess the same mass. The above facts account for the *law of constant composition:* the proportions by weight of the elements constituting a compound are always the same.

It has been shown experimentally that definite combining proportions by weight exist among the elements. This is shown diagrammatically in Fig. 9.1. Such a diagram could be extended to include the 98 known elements.

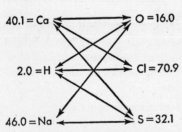

Fig. 9.1. Combining proportions among several of the elements.

52

Any two of the elements shown in Fig. 9.1 which combine to form a compound will do so in the ratio expressed by the quantities. That is, 40.1 grams of calcium will combine with 16.0 grams of oxygen to form 56.1 grams of calcium oxide; 46.0 grams of sodium will combine with 32.1 grams of sulfur to form 78.1 grams of sodium sulfide; and 2.0 grams of hydrogen will combine with 70.9 grams of chlorine to form 72.9 grams of hydrogen chloride. Observe that these combining proportions of the elements are either their atomic weights, as in the case of calcium, oxygen, and sulfur, or a multiple of their atomic weights, as with sodium, hydrogen, and chlorine. The elements will, of course, combine in amounts other than that expressed by their atomic weights, provided the ratios are the same as those given above.

Example 9.1. A piece of calcium weighing 2.16 grams was exposed to the air until oxidation was complete. (a) How much oxygen combined with the calcium? (b) What was the weight of the calcium oxide formed?

Solution. (a) From Fig. 9.1 we see that 40.1 g. of calcium combine with 16.0 g. of oxygen. Therefore:

$$\frac{16.0 \text{ g. O}_2}{40.1 \text{ g. Ca}} = \frac{x \text{ g. O}_2}{2.16 \text{ g. Ca}}$$

or
$$x = 0.862 \text{ g. O}_2.$$

(b) The weight of the calcium oxide would be the sum of the weights of the calcium and oxygen reacting. That is:

Weight of calcium oxide formed = 2.16 g. + 0.862 g. = 3.02 g.

The weight of oxide formed could have been obtained from the relationship that 40.1 grams of calcium combine with 16.0 grams of oxygen to form 56.1 grams of oxide. Then:

$$\frac{40.1 \text{ g. Ca}}{56.1 \text{ g. CaO}} = \frac{2.16 \text{ g. Ca}}{x \text{ g. CaO}}$$

or
$$x = 3.02 \text{ g. CaO}.$$

The combining proportions of the elements are related directly to the Avogadro constant N. For example, 40.1 grams of calcium and 16.0 grams of oxygen each contains N atoms (Sec. 8.4). This means that one atom of calcium combines with one atom of oxygen to form calcium oxide, CaO. On the other hand 46.0 grams of sodium contains 2 N atoms, and 32.1 grams of sulfur contains N atoms. Therefore, two atoms of sodium combine with one atom of sulfur. This is shown in the formula Na_2S for sodium sulfide.

Arbitrarily Established Combining Proportions

9.2. The Gram-equivalent Weights of the Elements. Since definite combining proportions have been shown to exist among the elements, it is evident that a standard of reference for combining powers would be convenient. The standard adopted is 8.0000 grams of oxygen, giving rise to the concept of *gram-equivalent weight*. The gram-equivalent weight is defined as the number of grams of an element which will combine with 8.0000 grams of oxygen. Since the combining proportions in Fig. 9.1 involve 16.0000 grams of oxygen, the gram-equivalent weights of the six elements shown would be one-half the combining proportions given. The concept is important since any two elements which react chemically will combine in amounts proportional to their gram-equivalent weights.

Example 9.2. The gram-equivalent weight of aluminum is 9.0 g. and of chlorine, 35.5 g. How many grams of aluminum will combine with 7.63 grams of chlorine?

Solution. The two elements will combine in amounts proportional to their gram-equivalent weights. Therefore:

$$\frac{9.0 \text{ g. Al}}{35.5 \text{ g. Cl}_2} = \frac{x \text{ g. Al}}{7.63 \text{ g. Cl}_2}$$

or
$$x = 1.93 \text{ g. Al.}$$

The gram-equivalent weights of the elements are determined experimentally.

Example 9.3. An analysis of magnesium oxide showed that 2.099 g. of the oxide contained 0.833 g. of oxygen and 1.266 g. of magnesium. From the above data calculate the gram-equivalent weight of magnesium.

Solution. By definition the gram-equivalent weight of magnesium would be the amount combined with 8.0000 g. of oxygen. Therefore:

$$\frac{1.266 \text{ g. Mg}}{0.833 \text{ g. O}_2} = \frac{x \text{ g. Mg}}{8.000 \text{ g. O}_2}$$

or
$$x = 12.16. \quad \text{Gram-equivalent weight of Mg.}$$

The gram-equivalent weight of any element has the same combining power as 8.0000 grams of oxygen. The gram-equivalent weight of hydrogen is 1.008 g., or 11,200 ml. at standard conditions. Use may be made of this fact to determine the gram-equivalent weight of a metal by displacement of hydrogen from acid solution. The amount of metal required to displace 1.008 g. of hydrogen, or 11,200 ml. at standard conditions, from an acid solution is the gram-equivalent weight of the metal.

Example 9.4. It was found that 0.450 g. of Al liberated 760 ml. of hydrogen from a solution of sulfuric acid, the gas being collected over water at 27° C. and 640 mm. of Hg. Calculate the gram-equivalent weight of aluminum from the data given in the problem.

Solution. One gram-equivalent weight of aluminum will displace 11,200 ml. of hydrogen at standard conditions. Evidently the first step in the solution will be to convert the collected gas to the volume it would occupy at standard conditions. Then:

$$V_{S.C.} = 760 \text{ ml.} \times \frac{273° \cancel{K.}}{300° \cancel{K.}} \times \frac{(640 - 27) \cancel{\text{ mm. of Hg}}}{760 \cancel{\text{ mm. of Hg}}}$$

$$= 558 \text{ ml. of } H_2, \text{ dry, at standard conditions.}$$

The amount of aluminum required to liberate 11,200 ml. of hydrogen can now be calculated by proportion.

$$\frac{0.450 \text{ g. Al}}{558 \text{ ml. } H_2} = \frac{x \text{ g. Al}}{11,200 \text{ ml. } H_2}$$

or $x = 9.0$.   Gram-equivalent weight of aluminum.

9.3. The Gram-equivalent Weight of an Element as Related to Oxidation Number. The gram-equivalent weight of an element may be determined from the oxidation number (or valence) of the element as it exists in a given compound. The oxidation number of the free element is, of course, zero. The following formula expresses the relationship between gram-equivalent weight, atomic weight, and oxidation number:

$$\text{Gram-equivalent weight} = \frac{\text{gram-atomic weight}}{\text{oxidation number}}.$$

Example 9.5. Determine the gram-equivalent weight of the metal as given in each of the following formulas: (a) NaCl, (b) CaCl$_2$, (c) Fe$_2$O$_3$.

Solution. First determine the oxidation number of the metal, then use the formula given above.

(a) NaCl. Oxidation number of Na = +1. Therefore:

$$\text{Gram-equivalent weight of Na} = \frac{22.997 \text{ g.}}{1} = 22.997 \text{ g.}$$

(b) CaCl$_2$. Oxidation number of Ca = +2. Therefore:

$$\text{Gram-equivalent weight of Ca} = \frac{40.08 \text{ g.}}{2} = 20.04 \text{ g.}$$

(c) Fe$_2$O$_3$. Oxidation number of Fe = +3. Therefore:

$$\text{Gram-equivalent weight of Fe} = \frac{55.85 \text{ g.}}{3} = 18.62 \text{ g.}$$

In each of the metals in Example 9.5, one gram-equivalent weight of the metal loses N electrons as the result of the formation of the compound from the elements.

22.997 g. Na = N atoms, each of which loses 1 electron.

20.04 g. Ca $\;= \dfrac{N}{2}$ atoms, each of which loses 2 electrons.

18.62 g. Fe $\;= \dfrac{N}{3}$ atoms, each of which loses 3 electrons.

The above may be summarized by the statement that one gram-equivalent weight of an element involves N electrons of that element when it enters into chemical combination with another element.

9.4. The Gram-equivalent Weights of Elements of Variable Oxidation States. It so happens that the atoms of two or more elements sometimes combine in more than one ratio, each combination occurring only under certain specified conditions. That is, some elements exhibit more than one oxidation state. For example, iron may exist in either the ferrous state, Fe^{+2}, or the ferric state, Fe^{+3}. It follows, therefore, that an element will have a gram-equivalent weight for each oxidation state it assumes.

Example 9.6. Determine the equivalent weight of iron in (a) $FeCl_2$, and in (b) $FeCl_3$.

Solution. Following the same procedure as in Example 9.5, we have:

(a) Gram-equivalent weight of Fe in $FeCl_2 = \dfrac{55.85 \text{ g.}}{2} = 27.93$ g.

(b) Gram-equivalent weight of Fe in $FeCl_3 = \dfrac{55.85 \text{ g.}}{3} = 18.62$ g.

Observe that the gram-equivalent weights for an element in its various oxidation states are in a ratio of small integer values. For example, for iron, as calculated in Example 9.6:

$$\frac{18.62}{27.93} = \frac{2}{3}.$$

The above small-integer ratio relationship is sometimes referred to as the *law of multiple proportions:* when two elements combine to form more than one compound, the weights of one combined with a fixed weight of the other element are in a ratio of small whole numbers. In Example 9.6 a fixed weight of chlorine, 35.457 g., is combined with 18.62 g. of Fe in $FeCl_3$, and with 27.93 g. of Fe in $FeCl_2$.

Example 9.7. Tin and oxygen combine to form two oxides. One contains 78.77 per cent tin and the other 88.12 per cent tin. Show that these figures are in accord with the law of multiple proportions.

Solution. To solve the problem it will be necessary to show that the combining ratios of tin are small integer values. Let us choose 1.00 g. of oxygen as the fixed weight. Then, in oxide No. 1:

$$\frac{78.77 \text{ g. Sn}}{21.23 \text{ g. } O_2} = \frac{x \text{ g. Sn}}{1.00 \text{ g. } O_2}$$

or $x = 3.71$ g. Sn combined with 1.00 g. O_2.

In oxide No. 2:

$$\frac{88.12 \text{ g. Sn}}{11.88 \text{ g. } O_2} = \frac{x \text{ g. Sn}}{1.00 \text{ g. } O_2}$$

or $x = 7.42$ g. Sn combined with 1.00 g. O_2.

The ratio 3.71 : 7.42 is as 1 : 2, which is in agreement with the law of multiple proportions.

Problems

9.1. When 5.81 g. of silver oxide was heated, 0.401 g. of oxygen was liberated. Calculate the gram-equivalent weight of silver. *Ans.* 108 g.

9.2. When 0.723 g. of iron reacted with a solution of H_2SO_4, there was liberated 340 ml. of hydrogen which was collected over water at 27° C. and 740 mm. of Hg. Calculate the gram-equivalent weight of iron.
Ans. 27.92 g.

9.3. Zinc oxide contains 80.3 per cent zinc. Calculate the gram-equivalent weight of zinc. *Ans.* 32.6 g.

9.4. When 1.391 g. of mercuric oxide was heated, 71.8 ml. of oxygen was liberated, measured at standard conditions. Calculate the gram-equivalent weight of mercury. *Ans.* 100 g.

9.5. When 0.590 g. of sodium reacted with water, there was liberated 314 ml. of hydrogen collected over water at 17° C. and 755 mm. of Hg. Calculate the gram-equivalent weight of sodium. *Ans.* 23 g.

9.6. A 4.00 g. sample of cupric oxide, CuO, was reduced to free copper by passing hydrogen over the hot oxide. The reduced copper weighed 3.20 g. Calculate the gram-equivalent weight of copper. *Ans.* 32.0 g.

9.7. Calculate the gram-equivalent weight of bismuth if 3.96 g. of the element forms 4.71 g. of oxide. *Ans.* 42.2 g.

9.8. Two oxides of copper contain respectively 20.1 per cent and 11.2 per cent oxygen. Show that the data are in accord with the law of multiple proportions.

9.9. Mercury and chlorine form two compounds. In one compound 0.669 g. of mercury is combined with 0.118 g. of chlorine; in the other compound 1.00 g. of mercury is combined with 0.355 g. of chlorine. Do these figures support the law of multiple proportions? *Ans.* Yes.

9.10 There are five oxides of nitrogen containing respectively 36.29, 53.25, 63.09, 69.49, and 74.01 per cent oxygen. Show that these figures are in accord with the law of multiple proportions.

9.11. An iron nail weighs 6.34 grams. What weight of rust, Fe_2O_3, would be formed by the nail? *Ans.* 9.06 g.

9.12. How much sodium and chlorine could be obtained by the decomposition of 12.0 grams of salt, $NaCl$? *Ans.* 7.28 g. Cl_2; 4.72 g. Na.

9.13. How much oxygen will combine with one gram of calcium? *Ans.* 0.40 g.

9.14. How much calcium will combine with one gram of oxygen? *Ans.* 2.50 g.

9.15. Calculate the gram-equivalent weight of the metal in each of the following compounds: Al_2O_3, CaO, Cu_2O, CuO, MgS, $SnCl_2$, and $SnCl_4$.

10

The Quantitative Significance of Chemical Formulas

Formulas are the fundamental expressions used by chemists to designate substances. The quantitative interpretation of formulas is the most basic and therefore the most important aspect of the study of chemistry. Such quantitative knowledge gives one a better appreciation of the science of chemistry. The quantitative interpretation of formulas is presented for substances existing in the solid, liquid, and gaseous states.

Some Quantitative Relationships Involving Molecules in the Gaseous State

10.1. The Mole Volume of Substances in the Gaseous State. An interesting relationship is shown when we compare the volumes occupied by one mole of gaseous substances under the same conditions of temperature and pressure. This relationship is shown for five gases in Table 10.1.

TABLE 10.1
THE MOLE VOLUME OF A NUMBER OF GASEOUS SUBSTANCES AT STANDARD CONDITIONS

Gas	One Mole	Weight of One Liter	Mole Volume at S.C.
O_2	32.00 g.	1.43 g.	32.00 ÷ 1.43 = 22.4 l.
N_2	28.02 g.	1.25 g.	28.02 ÷ 1.25 = 22.4 l.
H_2	2.016 g.	0.0899 g.	2.016 ÷ 0.0899 = 22.4 l.
HCl	36.47 g.	1.63 g.	36.47 ÷ 1.63 = 22.4 l.
CO_2	44.01 g.	1.965 g.	44.01 ÷ 1.965 = 22.4 l.

From the table we see that the volume occupied by one mole of each of the five gases at standard conditions is 22.4 liters, or 22,400 ml. The quantity 22.4 liters is called the *gram-molecular volume* (G.M.V.), and represents the volume occupied by one mole of any gas at standard conditions. Since one mole represents the weight in grams of 6.023×10^{23} molecules (Sec. 8.4), it follows that use may be made of the gram-molecular volume principle to determine the molecular weight of substances when in the gaseous state.

Example 10.1. It was found that 326 ml. of a gas weighed 0.492 g. at standard conditions. Calculate the molecular weight of the gas.

Solution. The molecular weight of the gas would be the weight in grams of 22,400 ml. at standard conditions. Then:

$$\frac{326 \text{ ml.}}{0.492 \text{ g.}} = \frac{22,400 \text{ ml.}}{x \text{ g.}}$$

or $x = 33.8.$ Molecular weight of the gas.

Example 10.2. It was found that 426 ml. of a gas weighed 0.492 g. at 27° C. and 640 mm. of Hg. Calculate the molecular weight of the gas.

Solution. Again, the molecular weight of the gas would be the weight of 22,400 ml. at standard conditions. However, the given volume of gas is not at standard conditions. We must, therefore, reduce the given volume to standard conditions. Then:

$$\mathbf{V_{S.C.}} = 426 \text{ ml.} \times \frac{273°\,K.}{300°\,K.} \times \frac{640 \text{ mm. of Hg}}{760 \text{ mm. of Hg}}$$

$$= 326 \text{ ml.}$$

The problem is now identical to Example 10.1. Compressing the 426 ml. of gas to 326 ml. volume would not change the weight of the mass of gas. The molecular weight of the gas is, therefore, 33.8 as in Example 10.1.

The gram-molecular volume principle may also be used to determine the weight of any given volume of a gaseous substance, providing its molecular weight is known.

Example 10.3. Determine the weight of one liter of hydrogen sulfide, H_2S, at standard conditions.

Solution. We know that one mole of H_2S, or

$$(2 \times 1.008) + 32.066 = 34.082 \text{ g.,}$$

occupies a volume of 22.4 liters at standard conditions. Therefore:

$$H_2S = \frac{34.082 \text{ g.}}{22.4 \text{ l.}} = 1.52 \frac{\text{g.}}{\text{l.}}$$

Example 10.4. Determine the weight of 375 ml. of oxygen at 23° C. and 740 mm. of Hg.

Solution. Since the gram-molecular volume principle applies only to standard conditions it will be necessary to reduce the given volume of oxygen to the volume it would occupy at standard conditions. Then:

$$V_{S.C.} = 375 \text{ ml.} \times \frac{273° \cancel{K.}}{296° \cancel{K.}} \times \frac{740 \cancel{\text{ mm. of Hg}}}{760 \cancel{\text{ mm. of Hg}}}$$

$$= 337 \text{ ml.}$$

We know that 22,400 ml. of oxygen weighs 32.00 g. at S.C. Therefore:

$$\frac{22,400 \text{ ml.}}{32.00 \text{ g.}} = \frac{337 \text{ ml.}}{x \text{ g.}}$$

or $\qquad x = 0.481$ g.   Weight of 337 ml. of O_2 at S.C.

Problems

10.1. One liter of chlorine gas at standard conditions weighs 3.214 g. Calculate the molecular weight of chlorine. *Ans.* 72.0.

10.2. Calculate the molecular weight of a gas, 225 ml. of which weighs 0.281 g. at standard conditions. *Ans.* 28.0.

10.3. Calculate the molecular weight of a gas, 642 ml. of which weighs 1.61 g. at 100° C. and 740 mm. of Hg. *Ans.* 78.8.

10.4. Calculate the weight of one liter of (a) ammonia, and (b) helium at standard conditions. *Ans.* (a) 0.76 g. (b) 0.18 g.

10.5. Calculate the weight of one liter of carbon dioxide at (a) standard conditions, and (b) 27° C. and 730 mm. of Hg. *Ans.* (a) 1.96 g. (b) 1.71 g.

10.6. A compound has the formula $COCl_2$. Calculate the weight of one liter of the gas at standard conditions. *Ans.* 4.42 g.

10.7. The molecular weight of a gaseous substance is 80. Calculate the volume occupied by one gram of the substance at standard conditions. *Ans.* 280 ml.

10.8. Calculate the weight of 350 ml. of CO_2 at S.C. *Ans.* 0.687 g.

10.9. When 0.700 g. of a substance was heated to 300° C., it formed 350 ml. of gaseous vapor. The barometric pressure was 72.4 cm. Calculate the molecular weight of the substance. *Ans.* 98.7.

10.10. Calculate the molecular weight of a substance, 2.810 g. of which formed 850 ml. of vapor at 200° C. and a reduced pressure of 60 mm. of Hg. *Ans.* 163.

Some Quantitative Relationships Involving Formulas

10.2. The Determination of the Formula of a Compound. In order to determine the formula of a compound, the following information must be available: (1) the elements constituting the compound; (2) the atomic weights of the elements; (3) the percentage composition of the compound; and (4) the molecular weight. All the above information must be obtained experimentally, but the details of the experiments need not be known in order to understand the calculations involved.

Example 10.5. A compound upon analysis was found to have the following percentage composition: carbon, 81.82 per cent; and hydrogen, 18.18 per cent. The molecular weight was found to be 44. Determine the formula of the compound.

Solution. The solution lies in finding the values of A and B in the expression C_AH_B. Since 81.82 per cent of the molecular weight is contributed by carbon and 18.18 per cent by hydrogen, then:

$$0.8182 \times 44 = 36 \text{ units contributed by carbon;}$$
$$0.1818 \times 44 = 8 \text{ units contributed by hydrogen.}$$

Next we must find how many carbon atoms are required to contribute 36 units to the molecular weight. This will be the value of A. Since one carbon atom contributes 12 units, its atomic weight, then:

$$36 \div 12 = 3 \text{ atoms of carbon} = A.$$

Each atom of hydrogen in the molecule contributes 1 unit to the molecular weight. Therefore:

$$8 \div 1 = 8 \text{ atoms of hydrogen} = B.$$

The formula for the compound is, therefore, C_3H_8.

Example 10.6. A compound was found to contain 40.01 per cent carbon, 6.67 per cent hydrogen, and 53.32 per cent oxygen. The molecular weight was found to be 178. What is the formula of the compound?

Solution. Following the same procedure as in Example 10.5, we will first determine the contribution of each element to the molecular weight, 178. Then:

carbon = $0.4001 \times 178 = 71.2$ units of molecular weight;
hydrogen = $0.0667 \times 178 = 11.9$ units of molecular weight;
oxygen = $0.5332 \times 178 = 94.9$ units of molecular weight.

The number of atoms of each in a molecule would be:

$$71.2 \div 12 = 6 \text{ carbon atoms;}$$
$$11.9 \div 1 = 12 \text{ hydrogen atoms;}$$
$$94.9 \div 16 = 6 \text{ oxygen atoms.}$$

The formula of the compound is, therefore, $C_6H_{12}O_6$.

As will be observed later, most methods for the determination of the molecular weight of a compound give only approximate values. The correct molecular weight of $C_6H_{12}O_6$ would be 180.16. This means that the contribution of each atom as calculated above may be somewhat in error and may, therefore, not represent an exact multiple of the atomic weight of the element. However, since a molecule must contain an integer number of atoms of each of the elements constituting the molecule, the inherent error in the experimental value must be taken into consideration. Observe that the nearest integer value was used in the second step above. On the other hand, methods of analysis have enabled chemists to determine percentage composition and atomic weights with a high degree of accuracy.

The term molecular weight has no significance when referred to ionic compounds (Sec. 8.1). The formulas for such compounds must, therefore, be determined without this information.

Example 10.7. A compound was found to contain 88.80 per cent copper and 11.20 per cent oxygen. The molecular weight has no significance. What is the formula of the compound?

Solution. Since the molecular weight has no meaning, the contribution of each atom to the molecular weight cannot be determined. It is possible, however, to determine the simplest ratio of atoms in the substance. First, divide the percentages given by the respective atomic weights of the elements. Then:

$$\left. \begin{array}{l} \text{Copper} = \dfrac{88.80}{63.54} = 1.40 \\[2mm] \text{Oxygen} = \dfrac{11.20}{16.00} = 0.70 \end{array} \right\} \text{Ratio of copper to oxygen atoms.}$$

Next, reduce the above ratio to the simplest integer ratio of atoms. These values represent the number of atoms of each element as expressed in the formula. Then:

$$1.40 : 0.70 = 2 : 1.$$

$$\begin{array}{cc} & \mid \quad \mid \\ & \mid \quad \text{oxygen} \\ & \text{copper} \end{array}$$

The formula is, therefore, Cu_2O.

Example 10.8. Red lead is composed of 90.65 per cent lead and 9.35 per cent oxygen. What is the formula for red lead?

Solution. The ratio of atoms would be:

$$\left. \begin{array}{l} \text{Lead} \quad = \dfrac{90.65}{207.21} = 0.437 \\[2mm] \text{Oxygen} = \dfrac{9.35}{16.00} \; = 0.584 \end{array} \right\} \text{Ratio of lead to oxygen atoms.}$$

Reducing the ratio $0.437 : 0.584$ to small integer values will evidently require more careful consideration than in Example 10.7. In this case trial and error is the best method. Evidently, one of the following integer ratios is the correct one.

$$\frac{0.437}{0.584} = \frac{1}{2} = \frac{1}{3} = \frac{2}{3} = \frac{1}{4} = \frac{3}{4}?$$

A few moments' inspection will show that:

$$\frac{0.437}{0.584} = \frac{3}{4}$$

or $0.437 \times 4 = 0.584 \times 3$ }   Proof for the validity of
and $1748 = 1752.$ }   a proportion.

The formula for red lead is, therefore, Pb_3O_4.

10.3. The Determination of the Percentage Composition of a Compound from the Formula.

The percentage composition of a compound for which the formula is not known must be determined experimentally by standard methods of chemical analysis. If the formula is known, then the percentage composition may be calculated.

Example 10.9. Calculate the percentage composition of water.
Solution.

$$\text{One mole of water} = (2 \times 1.008) + 16.000 = 18.016 \text{ g.}$$

That is, in 18.016 grams of water there are 2.016 grams of hydrogen and 16.000 grams of oxygen. Therefore:

$$\frac{2.016 \text{ g.}}{18.016 \text{ g.}} \times 100 = 11.19 \text{ per cent hydrogen}$$

and $$\frac{16.000 \text{ g.}}{18.016 \text{ g.}} \times 100 = 88.81 \text{ per cent oxygen.}$$

Example 10.10. What is the per cent of water in washing soda, $Na_2CO_3 \cdot 10 \ H_2O$?

Solution. First calculate the weight of one mole. Then:

$$\underset{(2 \times 22.997)}{Na_2} + \underset{12.01}{C} + \underset{(3 \times 16.000)}{O_3} + \underset{(10 \times 18.016)}{\cdot \quad 10 \quad H_2O} = 286.16 \text{ g.}$$

The weight of one mole is 286.16 grams, of which 180.16 grams is water. Therefore:

$$\frac{180.16 \text{ g.}}{286.16 \text{ g.}} \times 100 = 62.96 \text{ per cent water.}$$

Problems

10.11. Calculate the formula of a compound which contains 31.80 per cent potassium, 29.00 per cent chlorine, and 39.20 per cent oxygen.
Ans. $KClO_3$.

10.12. A compound was found to contain 42.11 per cent carbon, 51.46 per cent oxygen, and 6.43 per cent hydrogen. The molecular weight was found to be approximately 340. What is the formula of the compound?
Ans. $C_{12}H_{22}O_{11}$.

10.13. A compound was found to contain 32.00 per cent carbon, 42.66 per cent oxygen, 18.67 per cent nitrogen, and 6.67 per cent hydrogen. Calculate the formula if the molecular weight is known to be about 75. *Ans.* $C_2O_2NH_5$.

10.14. A gaseous compound was found to contain 75 per cent carbon and 25 per cent hydrogen. It was found that 22.4 liters of the gas at standard conditions weighed 16 grams. What is the formula of the compound? *Ans.* CH_4.

10.15. One liter of a gas was found to weigh 1.25 grams at standard conditions. Analysis showed it to contain 42.85 per cent carbon and 57.15 per cent oxygen. What is the formula of the compound? *Ans.* CO.

10.16. A compound was found to have the formula CH_2O, as calculated without knowledge of the molecular weight. Later the molecular weight was found to be approximately 177. What was the formula of the compound? *Ans.* $C_6H_{12}O_6$.

10.17. A sample of iron weighing 0.763 g. was burned in oxygen. The product weighed 0.982 g. What was the formula of the oxide formed? *Ans.* FeO.

10.18. A compound A upon analysis showed the following composition: potassium, 38.67 per cent; nitrogen, 13.85 per cent; and oxygen, 47.48 per cent. When heated a compound B was formed having the composition: potassium, 45.85 per cent; nitrogen, 16.47 per cent; and oxygen, 37.66 per cent. Write the equation for the reaction.

10.19. An oxide of iron contained 30.0 per cent oxygen. What was the formula of the oxide? *Ans.* Fe_2O_3.

10.20. A compound was found to contain 20.00 per cent hydrogen and 80.00 per cent carbon. It was found that 250 ml. of the gas weighed 0.256 g. at 27° C. and 640 mm. of Hg. What was the formula of the compound? *Ans.* C_2H_6.

10.21. Calculate the formulas of the following inorganic compounds:

(a) Na = 39.3%; Cl = 60.7%.
(b) Al = 15.8%; S = 28.1%; O_2 = 56.1%.

10.22. A gas is known to be one of the five oxides of nitrogen. Upon analysis it was found to contain 36.8 per cent nitrogen. What is the formula for the oxide? *Ans.* N_2O_3.

10.23. A gas had the composition 71.72 per cent chlorine, 16.16 per cent oxygen, and 12.12 per cent carbon. Oxygen diffused through a small opening 1.7 times faster than the gas analyzed. What is the formula of the gas? *Ans.* $COCl_2$.

10.24. The molecular weight of chlorine, as determined experimentally, is 72. What is the formula for chlorine? *Ans.* Cl_2.

10.25. The molecular weight of argon has been found to be 40. What is the formula for argon? *Ans.* A.

10.26. What is the per cent of aluminum in Al_2O_3? *Ans.* 52.9%.

10.27. Determine the percentage composition of formaldehyde, CH_2O, and glucose, $C_6H_{12}O_6$. *Ans.* C = 40%; H = 6.7%; O = 53.3%.

10.28. What is the per cent of water in borax, $Na_2B_4O_7 \cdot 10 \ H_2O$?
Ans. 47.2%.

10.29. What is the per cent of CaO in $CaCO_3$? *Ans.* 56%.

10.30. The bones of an adult person weigh about 24 pounds and are 50 per cent calcium phosphate, $Ca_3(PO_4)_2$. How many pounds of phosphorus are there in the bones of the average adult? *Ans.* 4.8 lb.

10.31. Washing soda is sold in two forms, as the anhydrous salt Na_2CO_3, and as the hydrated salt $Na_2CO_3 \cdot 10 \ H_2O$. Considering that the active constituent in washing soda is Na_2CO_3, which would be the cheaper to the consumer, the anhydrous salt at ten cents per pound or the hydrated salt at five cents per pound?
Ans. The anhydrous salt.

10.32. How much iron is there in one ton of iron ore containing 80 per cent hematite, Fe_2O_3? *Ans.* 1100 lb.

10.33. What is the per cent of copper in an ore containing 5.0 per cent of malachite, $CuCO_3 \cdot Cu(OH)_2$? *Ans.* 2.88%.

10.34. Calculate the per cent of available chlorine in bleaching powder, $CaOCl_2$, assuming that only one of the two chlorine atoms in the formula is liberated as free chlorine. *Ans.* 28%.

10.35. A compound was known to be either $CuCl_2$ or $CuBr_2$. A 5.00 g. sample yielded 2.36 g. of copper upon reduction. What was the compound? *Ans.* $CuCl_2$.

10.36. Lead dioxide, PbO_2, liberates one-half the oxygen atoms as free oxygen when heated. How much PbO_2 would be required to produce 10.0 g. of oxygen? *Ans.* 74.7 g.

10.37. How much oxygen could be obtained from one pound of mercuric oxide, HgO, assuming all the oxygen to be liberated upon heating?
Ans. 0.074 lb.

10.38. Calculate the formula of a compound, given that 55.85 g. of iron combines with 32.07 g. of sulfur. *Ans.* FeS.

10.39 A sample of copper weighing 3.18 g. formed 3.98 g. of oxide when made to react with oxygen. What is the formula of the oxide?
Ans. CuO.

10.40. How many gram-atoms of oxygen are there in 500 g. of Fe_2O_3?
Ans. 9.40.

11

The Quantitative Significance of Chemical Equations

Chemical equations consist of formulas. A quantitative interpretation of an equation is therefore a summation of such interpretation of the formulas constituting the equation. As with formulas, the quantitative study of equations may involve substances existing in the solid, liquid, or gaseous states. The economy of the chemical industry of the world is based upon the quantitative predictability of chemical changes as expressed by chemical equations.

Weight Relationships as Expressed by Chemical Equations

11.1. Introduction. Chemical equations express a definite weight relationship among the reactants and products in a reaction. Also, an equation indicates the manner in which the atoms of the reactants are rearranged to form the products. The above statements are supported by two fundamental facts: (1) atoms are the smallest parts of the elements involved in a chemical change, and (2) the atoms of each of the elements have fixed weights, excluding the variation due to isotopes, and always combine in the same ratio under similar conditions.

Since a symbol of an element represents a definite weight of that element, an equation can be interpreted in terms of definite amounts of reactants and products. In an equation the reactants and products contain the same number and kind of atoms. An equation also expresses volume relationships between reactants and products which are in the gaseous state. The preceding statements are summarized below.

	Zn +	H_2SO_4 →	$ZnSO_4$ +	H_2
Atoms.....	1	7	6	2
Molecules..	1	1	1	1
Moles.....	1	1	1	1
Grams.....	65.38	98.09	161.45	2.02
Liters (S.C.)	.....	.....	......	22.4

67

Observe that the weight of the reactants, 163.47 g., is equal to the weight of the products, 163.47 g.

Since chemical equations indicate weight and volume relationships, three types of problems will be discussed:

1. Problems involving weight;
2. Problems involving volume;
3. Problems involving both weight and volume.

11.2. Problems Involving Weight Relationships among the Reactants and Products.

Example 11.1. How many grams of zinc sulfate, $ZnSO_4$, would be formed by the action of 4.31 grams of zinc on sulfuric acid?

Solution. In solving problems based upon chemical equations, first write the equation involved. Next underscore the substances about which the problem is concerned, and designate the quantities of the substances as expressed in the equation. That is:

$$\underset{65.38 \text{ g.}}{\underline{Zn}} + H_2SO_4 \longrightarrow \underset{161.45 \text{ g.}}{\underline{ZnSO_4}} + H_2.$$

The problem designates the gram as the unit of weight to be used.

The above equation tells us that 65.38 g. of Zn will react with H_2SO_4 to produce 161.45 g. of $ZnSO_4$. From the law of definite composition we know that the ratio g. of Zn : g. of $ZnSO_4$ must be a constant. The next step is to set up the proportion, one ratio of which is given in the equation and the other in the problem. Then:

$$\frac{65.38 \text{ g. Zn}}{161.45 \text{ g. ZnSO}_4} = \frac{4.31 \text{ g. Zn}}{x \text{ g. ZnSO}_4}$$

or $$x = 10.6 \text{ g. ZnSO}_4.$$

Example 11.2. How many moles of Fe_2O_3 would be formed by the action of oxygen on one kilogram of iron?

Solution. The solution to the problem is based upon the equation:

$$\underset{223.4 \text{ g.}}{\underline{4 \text{ Fe}}} + 3 \text{ O}_2 \longrightarrow \underset{2 \text{ moles}}{\underline{2 \text{ Fe}_2O_3}}.$$

Observe that the problem requires the use of grams for iron and moles for Fe_2O_3. Then:

$$\frac{223.4 \text{ g. Fe}}{2 \text{ moles Fe}_2O_3} = \frac{1000 \text{ g. Fe}}{x \text{ moles Fe}_2O_3}$$

or $$x = 8.95 \text{ moles of Fe}_2O_3.$$

Example 11.3. The decomposition of 2000 pounds of limestone, $CaCO_3$, by heating would produce how much (a) quicklime, CaO, and (b) carbon dioxide, CO_2?

Solution. The unit of weight involved is the pound. Therefore:

$$\underset{\substack{100.09 \text{ lb.}}}{CaCO_3} \longrightarrow \underset{\substack{56.08 \text{ lb.}}}{CaO} + \underset{\substack{44.01 \text{ lb.}}}{CO_2} .$$

(a) Only two different substances may be involved in a given proportion. The two substances involved in this part of the problem are $CaCO_3$ and CaO. Therefore:

$$\frac{100.09 \text{ lb. } CaCO_3}{56.08 \text{ lb. } CaO} = \frac{2000 \text{ lb. } CaCO_3}{x \text{ lb. } CaO}$$

or
$$x = 1121 \text{ lb. } CaO.$$

(b) The two substances involved in this part of the problem are $CaCO_3$ and CO_2. Therefore:

$$\frac{100.09 \text{ lb. } CaCO_3}{44.01 \text{ lb. } CO_2} = \frac{2000 \text{ lb. } CaCO_3}{x \text{ lb. } CO_2}$$

or
$$x = 879 \text{ lb. } CO_2.$$

It is not always necessary to write the complete equation to solve a problem. For example, when silver reacts with nitric acid the silver is converted to silver nitrate, $AgNO_3$, with a number of other products, the reaction being somewhat complex. The products other than silver nitrate need not be indicated in the partial equation, provided they are not involved in the problem.

Example 11.4. Wire silver weighing 3.48 g. was dissolved in nitric acid. What weight of silver nitrate was formed?

Solution. Since the silver was converted to silver nitrate, we are interested only in the fact that one gram-atom of silver, 107.88 g., will form one mole of $AgNO_3$, 169.89 g. That is:

$$\underset{\substack{107.88 \text{ g.}}}{Ag} \longrightarrow \underset{\substack{169.89 \text{ g.}}}{AgNO_3} .$$

Therefore:

$$\frac{107.88 \text{ g. } Ag}{169.89 \text{ g. } AgNO_3} = \frac{3.48 \text{ g. } Ag}{x \text{ g. } AgNO_3}$$

or
$$x = 5.48 \text{ g. } AgNO_3.$$

Volume Relationships as Expressed by Chemical Equations

11.3. Problems Involving Volume Relationships among the Reactants and Products. One mole of a gaseous compound at standard conditions occupies a volume of 22.4 liters. Since an equation involves mole quantities of reactants and products, it follows that an equation may be interpreted in terms of volumes where gaseous substances are involved.   For example:

$$N_2 + 3H_2 \rightarrow 2NH_3.$$

Molecules	1	3	2
Moles	1	3	2
Liters	22.4	67.2	44.8

Observe that the ratio 22.4 l. N_2 : 67.2 l. H_2 : 44.8 l. NH_3 is the same as that of the number of molecules entering into the reaction, 1 N_2 : 3 H_2 : 2 NH_3.

Example 11.5.   How many liters of ammonia, NH_3, could be prepared from 750 liters of nitrogen, all gases being measured at standard conditions?

Solution.   From the above equation we see that 22.4 liters of nitrogen will form 44.8 liters of ammonia.   Therefore:

$$\frac{22.4 \text{ l. } N_2}{44.8 \text{ l. } NH_3} = \frac{750 \text{ l. } N_2}{x \text{ l. } NH_3}$$

$$x = 1500 \text{ l. } NH_3.$$

One could have obtained the above answer by inspection since, from the equation, we see that 2 volumes of NH_3 are formed for each volume of N_2 involved.

Example 11.6.   How many milliliters of CO_2 would be formed at standard conditions by burning 120 milliliters of ethane, C_2H_6?

Solution.   First write the equation for the reaction.

$$2\ C_2H_6 + 7\ O_2 \longrightarrow 6\ H_2O + 4\ CO_2$$

2 volumes			4 volumes
44.8 l.			89.6 l.
44,800 ml.			89,600 ml.

By inspection we see that twice the volume of CO_2 is formed as C_2H_6 burned.   Therefore, 240 ml. of CO_2 will be formed.   Solving by proportion, we have:

$$\frac{44,800 \text{ ml. } C_2H_6}{89,600 \text{ ml. } CO_2} = \frac{120 \text{ ml. } C_2H_6}{x \text{ ml. } CO_2}$$

or $x = 240 \text{ ml. } CO_2.$

11.4. Problems Involving Both Weight and Volume Relationships among the Reactants and Products.   This type of problem is a combination of the types discussed in Secs. 11.2 and 11.3.

Example 11.7.   What volume of oxygen at standard conditions could be obtained by heating 8.66 grams of potassium chlorate, $KClO_3$?

Solution. The equation for the reaction would be:

$$2\ KClO_3 \longrightarrow 2\ KCl + 3\ O_2 .$$
$$\underset{245.2\ g.}{} \qquad \underset{67.2\ l.}{}$$

Note that the problem requires the use of grams for $KClO_3$ and liters for oxygen. Therefore:

$$\frac{245.2\ g.\ KClO_3}{67.2\ l.\ O_2} = \frac{8.66\ g.\ KClO_3}{x\ l.\ O_2}$$

or

$$x = 2.37\ l.\ \text{of oxygen at S.C.}$$

Example 11.8. What volume of oxygen, collected at 27° C. and 740 mm. of Hg, could be obtained by heating 8.66 g. of $KClO_3$?

Solution. Note that this problem differs from Example 11.7 in that the oxygen is collected at other than standard conditions. Therefore, the value 2.37 l. obtained in Example 11.7 must be changed to the volume it would occupy under the conditions given in the problem. Then:

$$V' = 2.37\ l. \times \frac{300°\ K.}{273°\ K.} \times \frac{760\ \text{mm. of Hg}}{740\ \text{mm. of Hg}}$$

$$= 2.68\ l.\ \text{of}\ O_2\ \text{at 27° C. and 740 mm. of Hg.}$$

Problems

11.1. How many grams of sulfur will combine with 3.5 g. of copper to form CuS?   *Ans.* 1.8 g.

11.2. How many grams of iron would be required to replace the copper in 3.96 g. of copper sulfate, $CuSO_4$?   *Ans.* 1.39 g.

11.3. How many grams of iron would be required to replace one-half gram-atom of copper from a solution of copper sulfate, $CuSO_4$?

Ans. 27.9 g.

11.4. How many grams of copper would be precipitated by one gram of iron from a cupric salt in solution?   *Ans.* 1.14 g.

11.5. Calculate the number of grams of NaCl required to react with 100 ml. of 95 per cent H_2SO_4, density 1.84 g. per ml., according to the equation, $2\ NaCl + H_2SO_4 \longrightarrow 2\ HCl + Na_2SO_4$.   *Ans.* 209 g.

11.6. Calculate the volume of oxygen required to burn 60 liters of propane, C_3H_8, to CO_2 and H_2O, all gases being measured under standard conditions.   *Ans.* 300 l.

11.7. Under each substance in the following equation, indicate the number of grams represented:

$$6\ FeCl_2 + 14\ HCl + K_2Cr_2O_7 \rightarrow 6\ FeCl_3 + 2\ KCl + 2\ CrCl_3 + 7\ H_2O.$$

11.8. How many grams of $CrCl_3$ would have been formed from 0.78 g. of $K_2Cr_2O_7$ according to the equation given in problem 11.7?

Ans. 0.84 g.

11.9. How many grams of $FeCl_3$ would have been formed by the reaction of 5.0 g. of $FeCl_2$ according to the equation given in problem 11.7? *Ans.* 6.4 g.

11.10. Given the equation:

$$2\ Al + 3\ H_2SO_4 \longrightarrow Al_2(SO_4)_3 + 3\ H_2 \uparrow, \text{ calculate:}$$

a. The number of grams of $Al_2(SO_4)_3$ formed for each gram-atom of aluminum reacting. *Ans.* 171.07 g.

b. The number of grams of $Al_2(SO_4)_3$ formed for each mole of hydrogen formed. *Ans.* 114.05 g.

c. The number of moles of H_2SO_4 required for each mole of $Al_2(SO_4)_3$ formed. *Ans.* 3.

d. The number of grams of aluminum required for each liter of hydrogen formed at standard conditions. *Ans.* 0.803 g.

11.11. How many pounds of Fe_2O_3 could be obtained from 800 pounds of $Fe(OH)_3$? *Ans.* 598 lb.

11.12. How many grams of $BaSO_4$ would be precipitated by the action of H_2SO_4 on 2.68 g. of $BaCl_2$? *Ans.* 3.00 g.

11.13. How many pounds of water would be required to slake 50 pounds of CaO? *Ans.* 16 lb.

11.14. How many pounds of limestone, 80 per cent $CaCO_3$, would be required to make one ton of CaO? *Ans.* 4460 lb.

11.15. A portion of a silver coin weighing 2.44 g. and containing 90 per cent silver was dissolved in nitric acid. What weight of silver nitrate was formed? *Ans.* 3.46 g.

11.16. How many milliliters of nitric acid, density 1.21 g. per ml. and containing 34 per cent acid by weight, would be required to dissolve the silver in problem 11.15? Note: only 75 per cent of the nitric acid is used in converting the silver to silver nitrate. *Ans.* 4.17 ml.

11.17. How many tons of 95 per cent H_2SO_4 could be prepared from one ton of pyrites containing 90 per cent FeS_2, assuming all the sulfur to be converted to acid? *Ans.* 1.5 tons.

11.18. How many grams of 68 per cent HNO_3 could be prepared from 25 grams of $NaNO_3$ by the action of H_2SO_4? *Ans.* 27.2 g.

11.19. The CO_2 resulting from the burning of 0.325 g. of a compound in oxygen was passed through lime water, resulting in the formation of 1.08 g. of $CaCO_3$ as a precipitate. What was the per cent of carbon in the compound? *Ans.* 39.9%

11.20. What volume of CO_2 would be formed at standard conditions when one cubic foot of CH_4 burns to CO_2 and water? *Ans.* 1 ft.³

11.21. What volume of ozone would be formed from 960 ml. of oxygen temperature and pressure being constant? *Ans.* 640 ml.

11.22. Twelve liters of oxygen were partially converted to ozone. The resultant volume of the oxygen-ozone mixture was 11.8 liters. What volume of ozone was formed? *Ans.* 0.4 l.

11.23. What volume of oxygen, measured at 15° C. and 720 mm. of Hg, could be obtained from 18 g. of HgO? *Ans.* 1.04 l.

11.24. How many grams of $KClO_3$ would be required to produce 480 ml. of oxygen at 21° C. and 640 mm. of Hg? *Ans.* 1.37 g.

11.25. How many liters of hydrogen could be obtained by the action of steam on 100 g. of iron at 200° C. and 760 mm. of Hg? *Ans.* 92.7 l.

11.26. How many liters of hydrogen at S.C. would be required to reduce 80 g. of CuO to free Cu? *Ans.* 22.5 l.

11.27. How many milligrams of zinc would be required to prepare the hydrogen in problem 11.26 by the action of acid? *Ans.* 6.57×10^4 mg.

11.28. How much zinc would be required to prepare 500 ml. of hydrogen at 20° C. and 720 mm. of Hg? *Ans.* 1.29 g.

11.29. Calculate the weight of 39 per cent HCl required to prepare sufficient chlorine by action with MnO_2 to fill a cylinder of 3500 ml. capacity under a pressure of 20 atmospheres at 0° C. *Ans.* 1170 g.

11.30. How many grams of $(NH_4)_2SO_4$, reacting with $Ca(OH)_2$, would be required to prepare sufficient ammonia to react with 10 liters of HCl at S.C.? *Ans.* 29.4 g.

11.31. How many moles of CO_2 would be formed by burning 500 pounds of coal containing 96 per cent carbon? *Ans.* 1.8×10^4 moles.

11.32. What volume of hydrogen at 27° C. and 760 mm. of Hg will contain the same number of molecules as one liter of oxygen at standard conditions? *Ans.* 1.1 l.

11.33. How many moles of water will be liberated by the conversion of 500 g. of $CuSO_4 \cdot 5 H_2O$ to the anhydrous salt? *Ans.* 10.0 moles.

11.34. What weight of nitrogen will contain the same number of molecules as 2500 ml. of hydrogen at S.C.? *Ans.* 3.13 g.

11.35. What weight of lead will contain the same number of atoms as 1.00 g. of sulfur? *Ans.* 6.46 g.

11.36. How many grams of zinc reacting with H_2SO_4 will liberate the same amount of hydrogen as 2.30 g. of sodium reacting with water?
Ans. 3.27 g.

11.37. Sodium chloride weighing 1.225 g. was dissolved in 500 ml. of water. To this solution was added 1.700 g. of $AgNO_3$ in solution. How much AgCl precipitated? *Ans.* 1.43 g.

11.38. How many grams of iron can be oxidized to Fe_2O_3 by one mole of oxygen? *Ans.* 74.5 g.

11.39. What volume of hydrogen at standard conditions would be liberated by the action of 3.22 g. of zinc on 50 ml. of 40 per cent H_2SO_4, specific gravity 1.30? *Ans.* 1100 ml.

11.40. How many moles of CO_2, measured at 21° C. and 740 mm. of Hg, would be liberated by the action of 25.0 ml. of 20 per cent HCl, density 1.10 g. per ml., on 30.0 g. of marble containing 90 per cent $CaCO_3$? *Ans.* 0.075 mole.

11.41. How much SO_2 could be obtained from 16.033 g. of sulfur?

Ans. 32.033 g.

11.42. How many moles of SO_2 could be obtained from 25.0 g. of sulfur?

Ans. 0.78 mole.

11.43. How many moles of CO_2 would be formed by burning 120.1 g. of carbon? *Ans.* 10 moles.

11.44. How many grams of oxygen must be contained in a flash bulb to oxidize 0.25 g. of aluminum? *Ans.* 0.22 g.

11.45. How many gram-atoms of iron would be required to prepare five moles of Fe_2O_3? *Ans.* 10.

11.46. Given the equation, $2\ Fe + 3\ H_2O \rightarrow Fe_2O_3 + 3\ H_2$, calculate the following:

(a) 1.00 g. of Fe combines with _____ mole of H_2O. *Ans.* 0.0268 mole.

(b) 1.00 mole of Fe combines with _____ g. of H_2O. *Ans.* 27.0 g.

(c) 1.00 mole of Fe forms _____ g. of Fe_2O_3. *Ans.* 79.85 g.

11.47. How many grams of oxygen are required to prepare 100 g. of P_2O_5? *Ans.* 56.3 g.

11.48. A sulfuric acid plant uses 2500 tons of SO_2 daily. How many tons of sulfur must be burned to produce this amount of SO_2 gas?

Ans. 1250 tons.

11.49. How many grams of carbon could be oxidized to CO_2 by the oxygen liberated from 231.76 g. of silver oxide, Ag_2O? *Ans.* 6.0 g.

11.50. When 25.0 g. of Al was dissolved in HCl, the hydrogen was collected over water at 0° C. and 765 mm. of Hg. What was the volume of gas collected? *Ans.* 31.3 l.

12

Determination of the Atomic Weights of the Elements

The previous chapters fall into a somewhat natural sequence of study. The order of sequence of the remaining chapters could be varied since they are concerned with isolated phases of study generally considered to be a part of the first year course in college chemistry. Since atomic weights have been mentioned numerous times and their importance has been stressed, it may be of interest to present some of the experimental chemical methods which have been used to determine the atomic weights of the elements.

The Determination of Atomic Weights from Experimental Data

12.1. Determination of Atomic Weights from Chemical Analysis. A number of methods are available for the determination of the molecular weights of compounds. The methods, however, give only approximate values. Such approximate molecular weights are sufficiently accurate to use in determining the atomic weights of the elements constituting the compound. If the molecular weights of a number of compounds containing a particular element are known, together with the per cent of that element in each compound, then the atomic weight of the element may be calculated. Such calculated atomic weights are, of course, only as accurate as the values from which they were calculated. Table 12.1 illustrates the above. Column 4 was obtained by multiplying the molecular weight by the per cent of carbon.

Since an atom is the smallest part of an element that can enter into chemical combination, the smallest contribution of carbon to the molecular weight in a series of carbon compounds such as shown in Table 12.1 would represent the probable atomic weight of carbon. The data in the table thus indicate 12 as the atomic weight of carbon.

TABLE 12.1
THE ATOMIC WEIGHT OF CARBON FROM MOLECULAR
WEIGHT AND PER CENT COMPOSITION

Compound	Molecular Weight	Per cent Carbon	Carbon per Mole
CO_2	44	27	12
CO	28	43	12
C_6H_6	78	92	72
C_2H_2	26	92	24
CH_4	16	75	12
C_5H_{12}	72	83	60

It is possible to calculate more accurate atomic weights than by this method by chemical analysis, which gives the composition of a compound to the fifth decimal in grams (0.00000 g.). Atomic weights calculated from such data will give correspondingly accurate values.

Example 12.1. An analysis gave the composition of silver nitrate as 63.500 per cent silver, 28.255 per cent oxygen, and 8.245 per cent nitrogen. Calculate the atomic weight of silver with an accuracy consistent with the data given.

Solution. From the given data we will first calculate the formula for silver nitrate (Sec. 10.2). Then:

$$\text{Silver} \quad = \frac{63.5}{108} = 0.588.$$
$$\text{Nitrogen} = \frac{8.245}{14} = 0.589.$$
$$\text{Oxygen} \quad = \frac{28.255}{16} = 1.766.$$

These fractions reduce to the integer ratio 1 : 1 : 3. The formula is therefore $AgNO_3$.

From the formula $AgNO_3$ we see that there are 3 gram-atoms of oxygen associated with 1 gram-atom of silver. Therefore, the atomic weight of silver would be the number of grams of the element combined with $3 \times 16.000 = 48.000$ g. of oxygen. Therefore, using the data given we have:

$$\frac{63.500 \text{ g. Ag}}{28.255 \text{ g. O}_2} = \frac{x \text{ g. Ag}}{48.000 \text{ g. O}_2}$$

or
$$x = 107.88 \text{ g. Atomic weight of silver.}$$

The Determination of Atomic Weights from Gram-equivalent Quantities

12.2. The Determination of Atomic Weights from Gram-equivalent Weights. The gram-equivalent weights of most of the elements may be determined with a high degree of accuracy (Sec. 9.2), whereas most methods for the determination of atomic weights give only approximate values. Such approximate values, however, may be used to calculate more accurate atomic weights (Sec. 9.3).

Example 12.2. The gram-equivalent weight of magnesium was found experimentally to be 12.16 g. Its approximate atomic weight was found to be 24. Calculate a more accurate atomic weight for magnesium.

Solution. From the relationship (Sec. 9.3):

Gram-atomic weight = gram-equivalent weight $\times$ oxidation number

we see that the atomic weight of an element is a multiple of the gram-equivalent weight of the element. From the data given, the oxidation number of magnesium is $\frac{24}{12.16} = 2$. Therefore:

$$12.16 \times 2 = 24.32 \text{ g.} \quad \text{Atomic weight of Mg.}$$

12.3. The Determination of the Atomic Weights of Metals from the Amount of Combined Hydrogen Displaced by the Metal.
This method is essentially the same as that described in Sec. 12.2, since the method gives the gram-equivalent weight of the metal. One gram-equivalent weight of a metal will displace 1.008 grams of combined hydrogen.

Example 12.3. The approximate atomic weight of zinc is 65. It was found that 1.632 g. of zinc replaced 649 ml. of hydrogen measured at 27° C. and 720 mm. of Hg. Calculate a more accurate atomic weight for zinc.

Solution. As in Example 12.2, we must find the gram-equivalent weight and oxidation number of zinc from the data given. The gram-equivalent weight of zinc is the amount in grams which will displace 1.008 g. of hydrogen. Since one liter of hydrogen weighs 0.0899 g. at S.C., the given volume would weigh:

$$0.0899 \frac{\text{g.}}{\text{l.}} \times 0.649 \text{ l.} \times \frac{273° \text{ K.}}{300° \text{ K.}} \times \frac{720 \text{ mm. of Hg}}{760 \text{ mm. of Hg}} = 0.0503 \text{ g.}$$

That is, 1.632 g. of Zn will displace 0.0503 g. of H_2. Therefore:

$$\frac{1.632 \text{ g. Zn}}{0.0503 \text{ g. } H_2} = \frac{x \text{ g. Zn}}{1.008 \text{ g. } H_2}$$

or $x = 32.7$ g.   Gram-equivalent weight of Zn.

And   Oxidation state of Zn $= \frac{65}{32.7} = 2$.

Therefore, the atomic weight of Zn $= 32.7 \times 2 = 65.4$.

Problems

12.1. Calculate the approximate atomic weight of chlorine from the following data:

Compound	Molecular weight	Per cent chlorine
HCl	36	97
$CHCl_3$	119	89
PCl_3	138	78
$HgCl_2$	271	26
$MgCl_2$	95	75

Ans. 35.

12.2. Calculate the approximate atomic weight of hydrogen from the following data:

Compound	Molecular weight	Per cent hydrogen
Water	18.02	11.21
Hydrogen chloride	36.47	2.76
Benzene	78.05	7.75
Methane	16.03	25.01

Ans. 1.01.

12.3. Calculate the atomic weight of nitrogen from the data given in Example 12.1.   *Ans.* 14.01.

12.4. The gram-equivalent weight of chlorine was found to be 8.865 as calculated from an oxide of the element. Calculate (a) the atomic weight of chlorine using the data given in problem 12.1, and (b) the formula of the oxide.   *Ans.* (a) 35.46, (b) ClO_2.

12.5. Analysis showed that magnesium pyrophosphate, $Mg_2P_2O_7$, contains 0.1086 g. of magnesium to 0.2501 g. of oxygen. Calculate the atomic weight of magnesium as accurately as the data will permit.

Ans. 24.32.

12.6. An oxide of vanadium was found to contain 2.123 g. of vanadium for each 1.000 g. of oxygen. Calculate the atomic weight of vanadium, given that the approximate atomic weight is 50.   *Ans.* 50.95.

12.7. Sodium oxalate, $Na_2C_2O_4$, contains 34.325 per cent sodium and 47.764 per cent oxygen. Calculate the atomic weight of sodium.

Ans. 22.997.

12.8. The equivalent weight of zinc is 32.69. Its approximate atomic weight is 65. Calculate a more exact atomic weight.   *Ans.* 65.38.

12.9. An oxide of lead contains 13.377 per cent oxygen. Knowing the approximate atomic weight of lead to be 205, calculate a more exact atomic weight for the element.   *Ans.* 207.21.

12.10. The approximate atomic weight of aluminum is 25. Calculate a more accurate atomic weight, given that 1.332 g. of aluminum displaced 1.778 liters of hydrogen measured at 23° C. and 770 mm. of Hg.   *Ans.* 26.94.

13

Some Quantitative Relationships Involving Energy

With the advent of atomic energy the interrelationship between matter and energy has become common knowledge. Every chemical change and every change in state involves an energy change. The study of chemical changes, therefore, is not complete without the study of the energy changes accompanying them. Again, for better appreciation, the relationship between matter and energy, and the energy of chemical change, is presented from the quantitative viewpoint. Section 13.4 presents a purely physical method for the approximation of the atomic weights of the elements. Such physical methods are not so accurate as are the chemical methods discussed in Chapter 12.

The Relationship between Matter and Energy

13.1. The Einstein Equation Relating Matter and Energy. The equivalence between matter and energy was first postulated by Einstein in 1905. The interconversion of matter and energy is expressed in the following mathematical relationship:

$$E = (2.2 \times 10^{13}) \text{ g.}$$

| | grams of matter converted to energy
| constant relating matter and energy
energy in calories

That is, the conversion of one gram of any form of matter to energy would result in the release of 2.2×10^{13} calories. This quantity of heat would raise the temperature of 250,000 tons of water from 0° C. to 100° C. It is approximately the amount of heat obtained by burning 300 tons of coal. Modern developments in atomic energy support the early postulates of Einstein.

Units Used to Measure Quantity of Heat

13.2. The Calorie and the British Thermal Unit. Heat is a form of energy which may be measured quantitatively. The unit of heat energy used in the metric system is the *calorie* (cal.). For all practical purposes the calorie may be defined as the quantity of heat necessary to raise the temperature of one gram of water one degree centigrade. A larger unit, the *kilogram calorie* (kcal.), is equal to 1000 cal. The unit of heat energy used in the English system is the *British thermal unit* (B.T.U.), which is defined as the amount of heat necessary to raise the temperature of one pound of water one degree Fahrenheit.

Example 13.1. How many calories would be required to heat 125 g. of water from 23° C. to 100° C.?

Solution. By definition:

Calories = (grams of water) (° C. temperature change).

Therefore:

Calories = (125)(100 − 23) = 9625.

Example 13.2. How many B.T.U.'s. would be required to heat one gallon of water from 70° F. to 212° F.?

Solution. By definition:

B.T.U. = (lb. of water) (° F. temperature change).

Since one gallon of water = 8.3 lb., then:

B.T.U. = (8.3)(212 − 70) = 1179.

13.3. The Specific Heats of Substances. The *specific heat* of a substance is defined as the number of calories required to raise the temperature of one gram of the substance one degree centigrade.

TABLE 13.1

THE SPECIFIC HEATS OF SOME COMMON SUBSTANCES
IN CALORIES PER GRAM

Alcohol	0.581	Iron	0.107
Aluminum	0.214	Lead	0.031
Copper	0.092	Sulfur	0.137
Diamond	0.120	Water	1.000

Example 13.3. How many calories would be required to change the temperature of 125 g. of iron from 23° C. to 100° C.?

Solution. Note that the mass and temperature changes are the same as for the water in Example 13.1. However, the specific heat of iron is only 0.107 as compared to 1.000 for water. Taking specific heat into consideration, we have:

Calories = (grams) (° C. temperature change) (specific heat).

Therefore:

Calories = (125)(100 − 23)(0.107) = 1030.

Example 13.4. Calculate the specific heat of silver, given that 280 g. of the metal absorbed 136 cal. when changed from 22.13° C. to 30.79° C.

Solution. Solving the equation given in Example 13.3 for specific heat, we have:

$$\text{Specific heat} = \frac{\text{calories}}{(\text{grams}) \ (° \text{ C. temperature change})}$$

$$= \frac{136}{(280)(30.79 − 22.13)}$$

= 0.056 cal. per g. Specific heat of silver.

13.4. The Law of Dulong and Petit. Specific heats may be used to calculate the approximate atomic weights of elements, particularly the metals (Chap. 12). The law of Dulong and Petit states that the product of the atomic weight of a solid element and its specific heat is approximately 6.4. That is:

Specific heat × atomic weight = 6.4.

TABLE 13.2

THE RELATIONSHIP BETWEEN THE SPECIFIC HEAT AND
ATOMIC WEIGHT OF A NUMBER OF ELEMENTS

Element	Specific Heat	6.4 ÷ Specific Heat	Atomic Weight
Aluminum	0.214	30	26.97
Carbon	0.120	53	12.01
Iron	0.107	60	55.85
Magnesium	0.246	26	24.32
Zinc	0.094	68	65.38

Example 13.5. Calculate the approximate specific heat of silver.

Solution. From the law of Dulong and Petit:

$$\text{Specific heat of silver} = \frac{6.4}{107.88} = 0.059 \text{ cal. per gram.}$$

The experimentally determined specific heat for silver is 0.057 cal. per gram. This value agrees very well with the calculated value.

Example 13.6. The specific heat of gold has been found to be 0.031 cal. per g. The gram-equivalent weight of gold is 65.73 g. What is the atomic weight of gold?

Solution.

$$\text{Approximate atomic weight of gold} = \frac{6.4}{0.031} = 206.$$

$$\text{Oxidation number of gold} = \frac{206}{65.73} = 3.$$

Since the gram-equivalent weight is quite accurate, then:

$$\text{Atomic weight of gold} = 65.73 \times 3 = 197.2.$$

13.5. The Heats of Fusion and Vaporization of Substances. The temperature of a crystalline solid remains constant at the melting point until the solid is all melted. This shows that heat is required to melt a crystalline solid without changing its temperature. The *heat of fusion* is defined as the number of calories required to change one gram of a crystalline solid to the liquid state without a change in temperature. The heat of fusion of ice is 80 calories per gram.

Heat must be applied to a liquid at its boiling point in order to convert it to a vapor without a change in temperature. The *heat of vaporization* is defined as the number of calories required to change one gram of a liquid to vapor without a change in temperature. The heat of vaporization of water is 539 calories per gram.

Example 13.7. How many calories would be required to change 10.0 g. of ice at 0° C. to steam at 100° C.?

Solution. Three steps are involved in the solution of the problem:
(1) The heat required to melt the ice.

$$10.0 \text{ g.} \times 80 \frac{\text{cal.}}{\text{g.}} = 800 \text{ calories.}$$

(2) The heat required to raise the temperature to 100° C.

$$10.0 \text{ g.} \times 100° \text{ C. temperature rise} = 1000 \text{ calories.}$$

(3) The heat required to vaporize the water.

$$10.0 \text{ g.} \times 539 \frac{\text{cal.}}{\text{g.}} = 5390 \text{ calories.}$$

The total heat required would, therefore, be:

$$800 \text{ cal.} + 1000 \text{ cal.} + 5390 \text{ cal.} = 7190 \text{ cal.}$$

Problems

13.1. How many calories are there in one B.T.U.? *Ans.* 252 cal.

13.2. How many calories would be required to change the temperature of 250 g. of aluminum from 15° C. to 75° C.? *Ans.* 3210 cal.

13.3. How many calories would be required to change 25 g. of ice at −10° C. to steam at 110° C., given that the specific heat of ice is 0.51 cal. per g., and of steam is 0.48 cal. per g.?   *Ans.* 18,223 cal.

13.4. What is the temperature of a mixture of 50 g. of water at 20° C. and 250 g. of water at 40° C.?   *Ans.* 36.7° C.

13.5. Given 800 g. of water at 22° C., calculate the resultant temperature of the water following absorption of 3600 calories.   *Ans.* 26.5° C.

13.6. The resultant temperature of a mixture of 150 g. of water at 28° C. and 350 g. of copper at 100° C. was 41° C. Calculate the specific heat of copper.   *Ans.* 0.095 cal.

13.7. The specific heat of an element was found to be 0.100 cal. per g. It was found that 0.749 g. of the element formed 0.937 g. of oxide. Calculate the atomic weight of the element.   *Ans.* 63.6.

13.8. Ten grams of ice at 0° C. was placed into 100 g. of water at 50° C. What was the temperature after the ice had melted?   *Ans.* 38° C.

13.9. It was found that 144 cal. was required to change the temperature of 260 g. of aluminum from 20.00° C. to 22.50° C. Calculate the approximate atomic weight for aluminum.   *Ans.* 29.

13.10. How many calories of heat would be liberated if the temperature of 300 g. of iron was changed from 75° C. to 17° C.?   *Ans.* 1862 cal.

13.11. An oxide of iron was found to contain 30.06 per cent oxygen. When 400 g. of iron at 100° C. was mixed with 220 g. of water at 20° C., the resulting temperature was 33.0° C. Calculate the atomic weight of iron.   *Ans.* 55.83.

13.12. Given the specific heat of lead as 0.031, calculate the atomic weight of lead and compare to the accepted value.   *Ans.* 206.

13.13. When 350 g. of platinum at 100° C. was added to 250 g. of water at 16° C., the temperature of the resulting mixture was 19.5° C. Calculate the atomic weight of platinum.   *Ans.* 206.

13.14. Calculate the number of calories required to change the temperature of one atom of a metal one degree centigrade.
$Ans.$ 1.06×10^{-23} cal.

13.15. How many calories would be required to change 10.0 g. of ice at 0° C. to water at 15° C.?   *Ans.* 950 cal.

13.16. When one gram-atom of helium is formed from hydrogen in the sun, there is a loss of mass of 0.03 g. What is the energy in calories given off by the sun as a result of this loss of mass?   *Ans.* 6.6×10^{11} cal.

13.17. It is estimated that the sun loses 8000 tons of mass per second due to conversion of matter to energy. What is the caloric output of the sun per second?   *Ans.* 1.6×10^{23} cal.

13.18. How many calories would be required to change the temperature of 500 g. of water from 50° F. to 50° C.?   *Ans.* 20,000 cal.

13.19. How many calories would be required to change the temperature of one gallon of water one degree centigrade?   *Ans.* 3784 cal.

13.20. How many calories are liberated when one mole of steam at 100° C. condenses to water at 100° C.?   *Ans.* 9710 cal.

13.21. How many calories would be required to vaporize one mole of freon, CCl_2F_2, given that the heat of vaporization is 35.0 cal. per gram?   *Ans.* 4230 cal.

13.22. How many grams of freon would have to vaporize in a mechanical refrigerator to absorb sufficient heat to freeze 1000 grams of water in the freezing compartment?   *Ans.* 2290 g.

The Heat Involved in Chemical Changes

13.6. Heat of Reaction. Every chemical reaction involves an energy change, usually in the form of heat. Equations indicating such heat exchange are called *thermochemical* equations. When heat is liberated the reaction is *exothermic*, and when heat is absorbed it is *endothermic*. Since the heat exchange is proportional to the amounts of substances reacting, it has become necessary to set up a reference standard for heats of reaction. The *heat of reaction* is defined as the quantity of heat liberated or absorbed when one mole of a substance reacts. Two types of heats of reaction will be discussed: (1) heat of combustion, and (2) heat of formation.

13.7. Heat of Combustion. Combustion is the rapid reaction of a substance with oxygen, being accompanied by heat and light. *Heat of combustion* is defined as the quantity of heat liberated when one mole of a substance burns in oxygen. All combustion reactions are exothermic. For example:

$$C \quad + \quad O_2 \quad \rightarrow \quad CO_2 \quad + 94,400 \text{ cal.}$$

$$\begin{matrix} 1 \text{ mole} & 1 \text{ mole} & 1 \text{ mole} \\ 12.01 \text{ g.} & 32.00 \text{ g.} & 44.01 \text{ g.} \end{matrix}$$

The above equation tells us that when one mole of carbon, 12.01 g., reacts with one mole of oxygen, 32.00 g., to form one mole of carbon dioxide, 44.01 g., there will be liberated 94,400 calories of heat. Therefore, by definition, the heat of combustion of carbon is 94,400 cal.

Example 13.8. When 1.14 g. of sulfur was burned to SO_2, there was liberated 2464 cal. Calculate the heat of combustion of sulfur.

Solution. By definition the heat of combustion of sulfur is the heat liberated when one mole of sulfur, 32.066 g., burns to SO_2. Therefore:

$$\frac{1.14 \text{ g. S}}{2464 \text{ cal.}} = \frac{32.066 \text{ g. S}}{x \text{ cal.}}$$

or $$x = 69,300 \text{ cal.} \quad \text{Heat of combustion of S.}$$

Example 13.9. The heat of combustion of heptane, C_7H_{16}, is 1150 kcal. How many kcal. would be liberated by the burning of 500 g. of heptane?

Solution. One mole, 100.2 g., of C_7H_{16} will liberate 1150 kcal. Therefore:

$$\frac{100.2 \text{ g. } C_7H_{16}}{1150 \text{ kcal.}} = \frac{500 \text{ g. } C_7H_{16}}{x \text{ kcal.}}$$

or

$$x = 5.74 \times 10^3 \text{ kcal.}$$

13.8. Heat of Formation. The *heat of formation* is defined as the quantity of heat liberated or absorbed when one mole of a substance is formed from the elements.

Example 13.10. When 1.14 g. of sulfur was burned to SO_2, there was liberated 2464 cal. Calculate the heat of formation of SO_2.

Solution. From the equation:

$$S \; + \; O_2 \rightarrow SO_2 \; + \; \text{heat}$$
$$\text{1 mole} \qquad \text{1 mole}$$
$$\text{32.066 g.} \qquad \text{64.066 g.}$$

we see that one mole of SO_2 is formed for each mole of sulfur reacting. Therefore, the heat of combustion of sulfur and the heat of formation of SO_2 are numerically the same, 69,300 cal. This relationship exists in all reactions of direct combination of an element with oxygen.

Example 13.11. When hydrogen was burned in chlorine, 1000 cal. was liberated and 1.650 g. of HCl was formed. Calculate the heat of formation of HCl.

Solution. By definition, the heat of formation of HCl is the heat liberated when one mole, 36.47 g., of HCl is formed. Therefore:

$$\frac{1.650 \text{ g. HCl}}{1000 \text{ cal.}} = \frac{36.47 \text{ g. HCl}}{x \text{ cal.}}$$

or

$$x = 22,100 \text{ cal.} \quad \text{Heat of formation of HCl.}$$

13.9. The Measurement of Heat of Reaction. The experimental measurement of heat of reaction may be brought about by *calorimetry*. Many types of calorimeters are in use for such measurements. Fig. 13.1 shows the general construction of a bomb type of instrument.

Example 13.12. A sample of carbon weighing 0.463 g. was placed in the cup C in Fig. 13.1. The calorimeter was assembled and 2500 g. of water placed in the outer jacket D. As a result of burning the carbon, the temperature of the water rose from 22.54° C. to 23.82° C. The metal and glass of the calorimeter were equivalent to 350 g. of water in terms of their heat-absorbing ability. Calculate the heat of combustion of carbon.

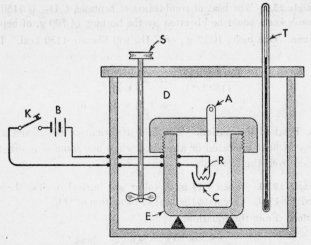

Fig. 13.1. The bomb calorimeter. The weighed sample is placed in the cup C, and the bomb E is filled with oxygen under pressure through the valve A. The outer jacket D is filled with water. S is a stirrer and T a thermometer. When K is closed the wire R becomes red-hot, causing the substance in the cup to burn. The heat is absorbed by the water, metal, and glass of the instrument. By means of the rise in temperature after ignition the heat of combustion of the substance in cup C may be calculated.

Solution. The heat of combustion of carbon would be the amount of heat liberated when 12.01 g. of carbon burns to CO_2. First calculate the heat liberated when 0.463 g. of carbon burns. The heat liberated raised the temperature of an equivalent of $2500 + 350 = 2850$ g. of water $23.82 - 22.54 = 1.28$ degrees centigrade. Therefore:

$$2850 \times 1.28 = 3648 \text{ cal. liberated by burning carbon, 0.463 g.}$$

Then:

$$\frac{0.463 \text{ g. C}}{3648 \text{ cal.}} = \frac{12.01 \text{ g. C}}{x \text{ cal.}}$$

or $x = 94,600$ cal.   Heat of combustion of C.

Problems

13.23. When 1.20 g. of benzene, C_6H_6, was burned to CO_2 and H_2O, 12.0 kcal. was liberated. Calculate the heat of combustion of benzene.
Ans. 780 kcal.

13.24. The heat of formation of water is 68.2 kcal. How many calories would be liberated by burning 12 g. of hydrogen?   *Ans.* 409 kcal.

13.25. Magnesium was burned in oxygen until one gram of MgO had formed. The heat liberated was 3.6 kcal. Calculate the heat of formation of MgO.   *Ans.* 145 kcal.

13.26. When 0.327 g. of carbon combined with sulfur to form CS_2, 0.691 kcal. was absorbed. Calculate the heat of formation of CS_2.

Ans. −25.4 kcal.

13.27. How many calories would be liberated by the complete combustion of 250 liters of CH_4 at S.C., given that the heat of combustion of CH_4 is 211 kcal.? *Ans.* 2355 kcal.

13.28. Given the equations:

$$2 H_2 + O_2 \rightarrow 2 H_2O \text{ (liquid)} + 136,760 \text{ cal.,}$$
$$2 H_2 + O_2 \rightarrow 2 H_2O \text{ (vapor)} + 117,420 \text{ cal.,}$$

calculate the heat of vaporization of water. *Ans.* 537 cal. per g.

13.29. Given the equation:

$$2 H_2 + O_2 \rightarrow 2 H_2O \text{ (ice)} + x \text{ cal.,}$$

calculate the value of x. *Ans.* 139,640 cal.

13.30. Given the equation:

$$N_2 + O_2 \rightarrow 2 NO - 43.2 \text{ kcal.,}$$

calculate the number of calories required to convert 25 liters of N_2 to NO at standard conditions. *Ans.* 48.2 kcal.

13.31. Given the equations:

$$C + O_2 \rightarrow CO_2 + 94.4 \text{ kcal.,}$$
$$2 CO + O_2 \rightarrow 2 CO_2 + 135.4 \text{ kcal.,}$$

determine the value of x in the equation:

$$2 C + O_2 \rightarrow 2 CO + x \text{ kcal.} \qquad Ans. \text{ 53.4 kcal.}$$

13.32. A sample of coal weighing 0.875 g., when burned in a calorimeter, liberated enough heat to raise the temperature of 2500 g. of water from 18.50° C. to 20.60° C. Calculate the B.T.U. value of the coal per pound. *Ans.* 10,810 B.T.U.

13.33. When 0.327 g. of carbon was burned to CO_2, 0.257 kcal. was liberated. Calculate the heat of formation of CO_2. *Ans.* 94.4 kcal.

13.34. How much heat would be liberated by 18 g. of carbon when burned to CO_2? *Ans.* 141.9 kcal.

13.35. When sufficient magnesium was burned in oxygen to form 5.0 g. of oxide, 18 kcal. was liberated. What is the heat of formation of MgO? *Ans.* 145 kcal.

13.36. How many calories are liberated when 1.00 g. of SO_2 is formed from the elements? *Ans.* 1082 cal.

13.37. The burning of 1.00 g. of sulfur to SO_2 resulted in the liberation of 2200 calories. Calculate the heat of formation of SO_2.

Ans. 70.6 kcal.

13.38. When 0.500 g. of coal was burned, sufficient heat was formed to raise the temperature of 1500 g. of water from 23.00° C. to 25.50° C.

Calculate the heat value of the coal in (a) calories per gram, and (b) B.T.U. per pound.

Ans. (a) 7.5 kcal. per g.   (b) 13,500 B.T.U. per lb.

13.39. How much heat would be liberated by the combustion of 2.5 pound-moles of carbon?   *Ans.* 1.07 × 10⁵ kcal.

13.40. How much heat would be liberated by the formation of one pound-mole of SO_2?   *Ans.* 3.15 × 10⁴ kcal.

14

A Study of Solutions

Many chemical reactions take place in water solution. Because of this it is necessary to establish standards for representing the strengths of solutions, a few of which will be discussed. Also there will be presented a number of experimental physical methods for determining the molecular weights of substances in water solution. An understanding of the experimental methods for the determination of atomic and molecular weights will give the student a greater appreciation of the meaning and usage of these terms.

Methods of Expressing the Strengths of Solutions

14.1. Standard Solutions. A *standard solution* is one the strength of which is known. That is, the amounts of solute and solvent in a given quantity of solution are known. A number of methods for expressing standard solutions have already been discussed, such as percentage by weight and by volume. Three other methods in common use for expressing the strengths of solutions are: (1) *mole fraction*, (2) *molarity*, and (3) *molality*.

14.2. Strengths of Solutions Expressed as Mole Fractions. *Mole fraction*, N, is defined as the fractional part of the total number of moles in a solution contributed by each component of that solution.

Example 14.1. A given solution contains 100 g. of salt, NaCl, and 900 g. of water. What are the mole fractions of the components of the solution?

Solution. Since the unit of concentration must be the mole, each of the given quantities of the components must be changed to moles. Then:

$$100 \text{ g. NaCl} = 100 \text{ g.} \div 58.45 \frac{\text{g.}}{\text{mole}} = 1.71 \text{ moles of NaCl}$$

$$900 \text{ g. H}_2\text{O} = 900 \text{ g.} \div 18.02 \frac{\text{g.}}{\text{mole}} = 49.94 \text{ moles of H}_2\text{O}$$

$$\text{Total number of moles} = \overline{51.65}$$

Therefore, by definition:

$$\text{Mole fraction of NaCl} = N_{NaCl} = \frac{1.71}{51.65} = 0.033$$

$$\text{Mole fraction of } H_2O = N_{H_2O} = \frac{49.94}{51.65} = 0.967$$

$$N_{NaCl} + N_{H_2O} = 1.000$$

Observe that the sum of the mole fractions of the components of a given solution equals one.

Mole fraction is an important method of expressing concentrations since it represents the ratio of particles of the components in the solution, a factor upon which many physical and chemical properties of solutions depend.

14.3. Strengths of Solutions Expressed as Molarity. *Molarity*, M, is defined as the number of moles of solute contained in one liter of solution. A one-molar, 1M, solution of NaCl, therefore, contains 58.454 g. of NaCl dissolved in sufficient water to make one liter of solution.

Example 14.2. How many grams of NaOH would be required to prepare five liters of 0.100M solution?

Solution.

Since   1.00 l. of 1M NaOH   = 40.005 g. NaOH,
then   1.00 l. of 0.100M NaOH = 40.005 × 0.100 = 4.001 g. NaOH,
and   5.00 l. of 0.100M NaOH = 4.001 × 5.00   = 20.005 g. NaOH.

Example 14.3. Calculate the molarity of a solution containing 8.82 g. of HCl in 100 ml. of solution.

Solution. By definition, the molarity is the number of moles of HCl per liter of solution. Therefore:

$$\frac{100 \text{ ml. solution}}{8.82 \text{ g. HCl}} = \frac{1000 \text{ ml. solution}}{x \text{ g. HCl}}$$

or $x = 88.2$ g. HCl per liter of solution.

Since   one mole HCl = 36.465 g.,

then $88.2 \text{ g.} \div 36.465 \dfrac{g.}{\text{mole}} = 2.42$ moles HCl per liter.

That is, the above solution is 2.42M with respect to HCl.

Example 14.4. How many grams of $Al_2(SO_4)_3$ are there in 300 ml. of 1.5M solution?

Solution.

Since   1.00 l. of 1M $Al_2(SO_4)_3$ = 342.14 g. $Al_2(SO_4)_3$,
then   1.00 l. of 1.5M $Al_2(SO_4)_3$ = 342.14 × 1.5 = 513.21 g. $Al_2(SO_4)_3$,
and   0.300 l. of 1.5M $Al_2(SO_4)_3$ = 513.21 × 0.300 = 154.0 g. $Al_2(SO_4)_3$.

14.4. Strengths of Solutions Expressed as Molality. *Molality,* m, is defined as the number of moles of solute per 1000 grams of solvent. A one-molal, 1m, solution of NaCl contains 58.454 g. of NaCl dissolved in 1000 g. of water.

Example 14.5. How many grams of NaOH would have to be added to 5000 grams of water to prepare a 0.100m solution?

Solution.

Since   40.005 g. of NaOH added to 1000 g. of H_2O = 1.00m solution,

then

40.005 × 0.100 = 4.001 g. NaOH added to 1000 g. H_2O = 0.100m solutior.,

and

5 × 4.001 = 20.005 g. NaOH must be added to 5000 g. of water to produce the required solution.

Example 14.6. Calculate the molality of a solution containing 8.82 g. of HCl dissolved in 100 g. of water.

Solution. The molality would be the number of moles of HCl dissolved in 1000 g. of water. Therefore:

$$\frac{100 \text{ g. } H_2O}{8.82 \text{ g. HCl}} = \frac{1000 \text{ g. } H_2O}{x \text{ g. HCl}}$$

or x = 88.2 g. HCl per 1000 g. H_2O.

Then   88.2 ÷ 36.465 = 2.42 moles HCl per 1000 g. H_2O.

That is, the above solution is 2.42m with respect to HCl.

Carefully compare the meanings of the answers obtained in Examples 14.2, 14.3, 14.5, and 14.6.

Problems

14.1. Calculate the mole fraction composition of a solution containing 500 g. of C_2H_5OH and 500 g. of H_2O.   *Ans.* C_2H_5OH = 0.28,
H_2O = 0.72.

14.2. Calculate the mole fraction composition of a saturated solution of NaCl at 0° C. At ° C., 35.7 g. of NaCl will dissolve in 100 g. of water.
Ans. NaCl = 0.099,
H_2O = 0.901.

14.3. How many molecules of solute are there in 100 ml. of a 0.100M solution?   *Ans.* 0.01N.

14.4. How many grams of NaCl are there in 250 ml. of a 2.50M solution?
Ans. 36.53 g.

14.5. What volume of 0.75M solution could be prepared from 500 g. of Na_2SO_4?   *Ans.* 4.70 l.

14.6. How many grams of water would have to be added to 1000 g. of sugar, $C_{12}H_{22}O_{11}$, in order to prepare a 1m solution?   *Ans.* 2924 g.

14.7. What is the molarity of a solution containing 250 g. of $CaCl_2$ in 1500 ml. of solution?   *Ans*. 1.50M.

14.8. What is the molality of a solution in which 250 g. of $CaCl_2$ is dissolved in 1500 g. of water?   *Ans*. 1.50m.

14.9. Calculate (a) the molarity, and (b) the molality, of a solution of K_2CO_3 which contains 22 per cent of the salt by weight and has a density of 1.21 g. per ml.   *Ans*. (a) 1.93M, (b) 2.04m.

14.10. One liter of 12M HCl is diluted to 20 liters. What is the molarity of the diluted solution?   *Ans*. 0.6M.

14.11. The acid solution in a fully charged lead storage cell contains 33 per cent H_2SO_4 by weight and has a density of 1.25 g. per ml. Calculate: (a) the mole fraction composition, (b) the molarity, and (c) the molality of the acid solution.

Ans. (a) N_{H_2O} = 0.917, (b) 4.21M, (c) 5.02m.

14.12. A solution of NaCl contained 30 g. of NaCl in 1500 ml. of solution. What was the molarity of the solution?   *Ans*. 0.34M.

14.13. How many grams of KBr could be obtained by evaporating 50 ml. of a 0.50M solution of the salt?   *Ans*. 2.98g.

14.14. What would be the molarity of a solution prepared by adding 500 ml. of water to 100 ml. of 0.60M solution?   *Ans*. 0.10M.

14.15. Calculate the molarity of a solution in which 50 liters of HCl gas measured at standard conditions is dissolved in 2.0 liters of water. Assume no change in volume.   *Ans*. 1.12M.

14.16. How many molecules of sugar would there be in 1.00 ml. of 1.00M solution?   *Ans*. 6.023×10^{20}

The Determination of the Molecular Weights of Substances in Solution

14.5. Introduction. Solutions of the same molality contain the same ratio of solute to solvent molecules. For example, in a one-molal water solution there is one solute molecule for every 55.5 molecules of water, since:

$$1 \text{ mole of solute} = N \text{ molecules,}$$

and $$1000 \text{ g. } H_2O = \frac{1000}{18.016} = 55.5 \text{ moles} = 55.5N \text{ molecules.}$$

The addition of an impurity to a liquid such as water will affect certain physical properties of the liquid in direct proportion to the number of particles present. The vapor pressure is a physical property of water so affected. The vapor pressure of water in turn determines the freezing point and boiling point of the solution. The discussion which follows will show how the molecular weight of the solute may be determined from the *freezing-point lowering* and the *boiling-point elevation* of water solutions. In order that the above be valid, it is necessary that the solute be a nonionic compound, nonreactive with water, and nonvolatile.

14.6. Determination of the Molecular Weight of the Solute from the Freezing-point Lowering. The addition of one mole of solute to 1000 grams of water produces a solution freezing at $-1.86°$ C. This quantity, $1.86°$ C., is called the *molecular freezing-point lowering constant* for water. The constant is different for different liquids. The addition of one mole of methyl alcohol, $CH_3OH = 32$ g., or one mole of sugar, $C_{12}H_{22}O_{11} = 342$ g., to 1000 g. of water produces a solution which freezes at $-1.86°$ C. The freezing point of a 0.100m solution would be one-tenth this amount, or $-0.186°$ C. This would be expected since the number of solute molecules in the latter solution is only one-tenth that in a one-molal solution.

The above relationships hold only for very dilute solutions. Solutions actually containing one mole of solute in 1000 grams of water would give experimental values quite different from the calculated values. Solutions of such strength are used only as reference concentrations.

Example 14.7. Calculate the molecular weight of urea, given that 4.00 g. dissolved in 1000 g. of water produces a solution freezing at $-0.124°$ C.

Solution. Two principles are involved: (1) the lowering of the freezing point is directly proportional to the molal concentration, and (2) one mole of urea dissolved in 1000 g. of water would give a solution freezing at $-1.86°$ C. Then:

$$\frac{4.00 \text{ g. urea}}{0.124° \text{ C.}} = \frac{x \text{ g. urea}}{1.86° \text{ C.}}$$

or $x = 60$ g.   Molecular weight of urea, CON_2H_4.

Example 14.8. Calculate the molecular weight of a substance, 1.00 g. of which dissolved in 250 g. of water produces a solution freezing at $-0.124°$ C.

Solution. In order to use the molecular freezing-point lowering constant, all calculations must be based upon grams of solute per 1000 g. of water. Therefore:

$$\frac{1.00 \text{ g. solute}}{250 \text{ g. H}_2O} = \frac{x \text{ g. solute}}{1000 \text{ g. H}_2O}$$

or $x = 4.00$ g. solute per 1000 g. H_2O.

The problem is now identical to Example 14.7. The molecular weight of the solute is, therefore, 60.

Example 14.9. Calculate the freezing point of a solution containing 10.0 g. of alcohol, C_2H_5OH, dissolved in 1000 g. of water.

Solution. One mole of ethyl alcohol, 46 g., dissolved in 1000 g. of water would give a solution freezing at $-1.86°$ C. Any other concentration would lower the freezing point proportionately. Therefore:

$$\frac{46 \text{ g. } C_2H_5OH}{1.86° \text{ C.}} = \frac{10.0 \text{ g. } C_2H_5OH}{x° \text{ C.}}$$

or $x = 0.40°$ C.

That is, the freezing point of the solution would be $-0.40°$ C.

14.7. Determination of the Molecular Weight of the Solute from the Boiling-point Elevation. The vapor pressure of a solution is always less than that of the pure solvent, provided the solute is non-volatile. The boiling point of a solution is, therefore, always higher than the boiling point of the solvent. One mole of solute dissolved in 1000 grams of water will result in a solution boiling at $100.52°$ C. at one atmosphere pressure. This increase in boiling point, $0.52°$ C., is called the *molecular boiling-point elevation constant* for water. The same relationships exist between the freezing-point lowering and concentration as exist between the boiling-point elevation and concentration.

Example 14.10. Calculate the molecular weight of a substance, 4.80 g. of which dissolved in 240 g. of water gave a solution boiling at $100.065°$ C. at a pressure of one atmosphere.

Solution. First calculate the concentration in grams of solute per 1000 grams of water. Then:

$$\frac{4.80 \text{ g. solute}}{240 \text{ g. } H_2O} = \frac{x \text{ g. solute}}{1000 \text{ g. } H_2O}$$

or $x = 20.0$ g. solute per 1000 g. H_2O.

Next calculate the concentration required to produce a boiling-point elevation of $0.52°$ C. This will be the molecular weight of the solute. That is:

$$\frac{20.0 \text{ g. solute}}{0.065° \text{ C.}} = \frac{x \text{ g. solute}}{0.52° \text{ C.}}$$

or $x = 160$ g. Molecular weight of solute.

Problems

14.17. A solution containing 2 g. of sugar in 100 g. of water freezes at $-0.11°$ C. What would be the freezing point of a solution containing 4 g. of sugar in 100 g. of water?   *Ans.* $-0.22°$ C.

14.18. Calculate the molecular weight of a substance, 0.41 g. of which dissolved in 1000 g. of water lowered the freezing point 0.016° C.

Ans. 48.

14.19. Calculate the molecular weight of a substance, 1.34 g. of which dissolved in 125 g. of water elevated the boiling point 0.071° C.

Ans. 78.

14.20. Calculate the freezing point of the solution given in problem 14.19.

Ans. −0.26° C.

14.21. Calculate the boiling point of a solution containing 4.0 g. of sugar, $C_{12}H_{22}O_{11}$, in 250 ml. of water at one atmosphere pressure.

Ans. 100.024° C.

14.22. Calculate the freezing point of a solution containing 6.0 g. of urea, CON_2H_4, dissolved in 500 g. of water. *Ans.* −0.37° C.

14.23. Calculate the molecular weight of a substance, 2.12 g. of which dissolved in 180 g. of water freezes at −0.118° C. *Ans.* 186.

14.24. Calculate the boiling point of the solution given in problem 14.23, at one atmosphere pressure. *Ans.* 100.033° C.

14.25. Find the molecular weight of a compound, 1.21 g. of which dissolved in 60 g. of water gave a solution boiling at 212.38° F. at a pressure of one atmosphere. *Ans.* 50.

14.26. Calculate the freezing point of the solution given in problem 14.25.

Ans. 30.67° F.

14.27. What weight of urea, CON_2H_4, must be dissolved in 500 g. of water to produce the same lowering of the freezing point as 1.50 g. of sugar, $C_{12}H_{22}O_{11}$, dissolved in 250 g. of water? *Ans.* 0.53 g.

14.28. How much glycerine, $C_3H_8O_3$, must be dissolved in 800 g. of water to produce a freezing-point lowering of 0.186° C.? *Ans.* 7.36 g.

14.29. A 1 per cent solution of each of two compounds A and B is prepared. The freezing-point lowering of A is twice that of B. How do their molecular weights compare? *Ans.* B twice that of A.

14.30. Calculate the boiling point of a water solution containing one-tenth mole of a substance dissolved in 400 ml. of water, pressure one atmosphere. *Ans.* 100.13° C.

14.31. Calculate the freezing point of the solution in problem 14.30.

Ans. −0.465° C.

14.32. Calculate the freezing points of the following solutions:

(a) Two quarts of alcohol, C_2H_5OH, density 0.79 g. per ml., mixed with 8 quarts of water. *Ans.* 17.6° F.

(b) Two quarts of glycol, $C_2H_6O_2$, density 1.10 g. per ml., mixed with 8 quarts of water. *Ans.* 17.1° F.

14.33. Calculate the boiling point of a 5 per cent sugar solution, $C_{12}H_{22}O_{11}$.

Ans. 100.080° C.

14.34. How many grams of methyl alcohol, CH_3OH, would have to be dissolved in 5000 g. of water to produce a solution with a freezing-point lowering of 10° C.? *Ans.* 860 g.

14.35. What would be the freezing point of a solution containing 0.40 mole of CH_3OH dissolved in 800 g. of water?   *Ans.* −0.93° C.

14.36. What would be the boiling point at 760 mm. of Hg of a solution containing one mole of solute dissolved in 55.5 moles of water?

Ans. 100.52° C.

14.37. What would be the ratio of solute to water molecules in a 0.100m solution?   *Ans.* 1 : 555.

14.38. How would the ratio of solute to water molecules compare in 0.5m and 1.0m solutions?   *Ans.* 1 : 2.

14.39. When one mole of a substance was dissolved in 1000 g. of water, the resultant volume was 1030 ml. How many molecules of solute would there be in one ml. of the solution?   *Ans.* 5.8×10^{20}.

14.40. How many molecules of solvent are there per milliliter in the solution in problem 14.39?   *Ans.* 3.2×10^{22}.

15

Chemical Equilibria

The concept of equilibrium is a new one so far as previous discussions are concerned. Many chemical reactions do not go to completion. That is, the products react, thus setting up a state of equilibrium between reactants and products, there being a definite distribution among the reacting substances for any given conditions. A knowledge of the concentrations of the reacting substances at equilibrium is important, therefore, in industries dependent upon a chemical change to produce a marketable product. Chemical equilibria may involve substances in the solid, liquid, or gaseous states. All plant and animal tissues depend upon specific chemical equilibria to function properly, thereby affecting our very existence. Sections 15.7 and 15.8 extend the concept of gram-equivalent weight to compounds in solution.

Gaseous Equilibria

15.1. Introduction. Chemical equilibria involve two opposing processes occurring simultaneously and at the same rate. By *rate of reaction* is meant the amount of reacting material converted to products in a given period of time. Amounts are usually given in moles, and time in seconds.

A chemical equilibrium may be represented by the general equation:

$$A + B \underset{S_2}{\overset{S_1}{\rightleftharpoons}} C + D.$$

In the above reaction S_1 represents the rate of the forward reaction, and S_2 the rate of the reverse reaction.

15.2. The Equilibrium Constant. At equilibrium $S_1 = S_2$. The equilibrium constant for the general reaction given in Sec. 15.1 would be:

$$K = \frac{(C)(D)}{(A)(B)},$$

where K is called the *equilibrium constant*.

A more general equilibrium equation would be:

$$aA + bB \underset{S_2}{\overset{S_1}{\rightleftharpoons}} cC + dD,$$

for which

$$K = \frac{(C)^c(D)^d}{(A)^a(B)^b}.$$

The value of K for any given reaction is essentially a constant at any given temperature. Note that the value of K is independent of the concentrations of the reacting substances. Any change in the concentrations of the reacting substances by the addition or removal of reacting substances will so shift the equilibrium as to maintain K constant for that temperature. It is evident that the addition of C or D will shift the equilibrium to the left, and the removal of C or D will shift the equilibrium to the right, in either case the value of K remaining constant. Evidently when K is large, C and D predominate; when K is small, A and B predominate.

Example 15.1. A closed reaction chamber containing PCl_5 was heated to 230° C. at one atmosphere pressure until equilibrium had been established. Analysis showed the following concentrations in the reaction chamber: $(PCl_5) = 0.45$ mole per liter, $(PCl_3) = (Cl_2) = 0.096$ mole per liter. Calculate K for the reaction $PCl_5 \rightleftharpoons PCl_3 + Cl_2$.

Solution. The equilibrium constant K for the reaction is given by the expression:

$$K = \frac{(PCl_3)(Cl_2)}{(PCl_5)}.$$

Substituting the given concentrations in the above, we have:

$$K = \frac{(0.096)(0.096)}{(0.45)} = 0.0205 \text{ at } 230° \text{ C.}$$

Example 15.2. Quantities of PCl_3 and Cl_2 were placed in a reaction chamber and heated to 230° C. at one atmosphere pressure. At equilibrium $(PCl_5) = 0.235$ mole per liter, and $(PCl_3) = 0.174$ mole per liter. Calculate (Cl_2).

Solution. For the given reaction at 230° C., K = 0.0205. Solving the equilibrium constant expression for (Cl_2), and substituting concentration values, we have:

$$(Cl_2) = \frac{K \times (PCl_5)}{(PCl_3)} = \frac{(0.0205)(0.235)}{(0.174)} = 0.028 \text{ mole per liter.}$$

Example 15.3. One liter of HI was heated at 500° C. and constant pressure until equilibrium had been established according to the equation

2 HI $\rightleftharpoons$ H$_2$ + I$_2$. Analysis showed the following concentrations in the reaction chamber: (H$_2$) = 0.42 mole per liter, (I$_2$) = 0.42 mole per liter, and (HI) = 3.52 mole per liter. Calculate the value of K for the above equation at 500° C.

Solution. For the given equation:

$$K = \frac{(H_2)(I_2)}{(HI)^2} = \frac{(0.42)(0.42)}{(3.52)^2} = 0.014 \text{ at } 500° \text{ C.}$$

Example 15.4. One mole of HI is introduced into the system in equilibrium in Example 15.3. Calculate the concentrations of H$_2$, I$_2$, and HI after the system has again reached equilibrium at 500° C.

Solution. The addition of one mole of HI would tend to increase the denominator in the expression for K, thereby decreasing the value of K. In order to retain a constant value for K, the system reacts by further dissociation of HI.

Let x = moles of HI dissociating to maintain K a constant.

Then, for each mole of HI dissociating, there will be formed 0.50 mole each of H$_2$ and I$_2$. Therefore:

$0.50x$ = moles each of H$_2$ and I$_2$ formed to maintain K constant.

At the new equilibrium:

$$(H_2) = (I_2) = 0.42 + 0.50x$$

and $$(HI) = 3.52 + 1.00 - x.$$

Substituting the above values in the equilibrium equation gives:

$$0.014 = \frac{(0.42 + 0.50x)(0.42 + 0.50x)}{(3.52 + 1.00 - x)^2}.$$

Simplifying and collecting like terms gives:

$$0.24x^2 + 0.55x - 0.11 = 0.$$

Solving the quadratic equation for x gives (Sec. 3.13):

$$x = \frac{-0.55 \pm \sqrt{(0.55)^2 - (4)(0.24)(-0.11)}}{(2)(0.24)}$$

$$= 0.17 \text{ or } -2.3.$$

A negative value has no significance. Therefore, 0.17 mole of HI would dissociate to maintain K constant. Then, under the new equilibrium conditions:

(H$_2$) = 0.42 + 0.50x = 0.42 + 0.09 = 0.51 mole per liter,
(I$_2$) = 0.42 + 0.50x = 0.42 + 0.09 = 0.51 mole per liter,
(HI) = 3.52 + 1.00 - x = 3.52 + 1.00 - 0.17 = 4.35 moles per liter.

The validity of the above values may be checked by substituting in the original equation. Then:

$$\frac{(0.51)(0.51)}{(4.35)^2} = 0.014 = K.$$

That is, the value of K has been maintained constant by the system in equilibrium.

Problems

15.1. Given the equation $A \rightleftharpoons B + C$, calculate K if, at equilibrium, A = 4.6 moles per liter, and B = C = 2.3 moles per liter.

Ans. 1.15.

15.2. Two moles of B were introduced into the system in equilibrium in problem 15.1. Calculate (A), (B), and (C) after equilibrium has again been attained. *Ans.* 3.6, 3.3, 1.3.

15.3. Two moles of A were removed from the system in equilibrium in problem 15.1. Calculate (A), (B), and (C) at the new equilibrium.

Ans. 3.0, 1.9, 1.9.

15.4. Analysis showed the following concentrations at 440° C. for the equilibrium $2 HI \rightleftharpoons H_2 + I_2$. Is K a constant at 440° C.?

	(H_2)	(I_2)	(HI)
Trial 1	0.0317	0.0806	0.347
Trial 2	0.0097	0.333	0.390

Ans. 0.0213, 0.0212.

15.5. The following concentrations were obtained at 5000° C. for the reaction in problem 15.4: (H_2) = 0.22, (I_2) = 0.22, and (HI) = 1.38. How does temperature affect the value of K? *Ans.* 0.0255.

15.6. K is equal to 69 for the reaction $N_2 + 3 H_2 \rightleftharpoons 2 NH_3$ at 500° C. Analysis of a seven-liter container showed that, at 500° C., there were present 3.71 moles of hydrogen and 4.55 moles of ammonia. How many moles of nitrogen were there in the container?

Ans. 0.288 mole.

15.7. PCl_5 is 40 per cent dissociated at a given temperature according to the equation $PCl_5 \rightleftharpoons PCl_3 + Cl_2$. What is the percentage increase in the number of particles in the container due to the dissociation of the PCl_5? *Ans.* 40%.

15.8. At 1500° C. water is 5 per cent dissociated according to the equation $2 H_2O \rightleftharpoons 2 H_2 + O_2$. Calculate K for water at 1500° C. Note: assume a concentration of one mole of water per liter before dissociation. *Ans.* 0.000069.

15.9. If there had been one mole of water in the reaction chamber in problem 15.8, calculate the number of molecules of H_2O, H_2, and O_2 present at equilibrium at 1500° C. *Ans.* 0.95N, 0.05N, 0.025N.

Ionic Equilibria in Solution

15.3. The Ionization Constants of Acids and Bases. Certain covalent compounds such as HCl and NH_4OH undergo partial ionization when in water solution. An equilibrium is thus established between ionized and nonionized molecules. The equilibrium constant principle (Sec. 15.2) may, therefore, be applied to such ionization equations. For example, the ionization equations for acetic acid, $HC_2H_3O_2$, and ammonium hydroxide, NH_4OH, and the equilibrium expressions for the reactions would be:

$$HC_2H_3O_2 \rightleftharpoons H^+ + C_2H_3O_2^-,$$

and $\qquad K_a = \dfrac{(H^+)(C_2H_3O_2^-)}{(HC_2H_3O_2)} = 1.84 \times 10^{-5}$ at 25° C.;

$$NH_4OH \rightleftharpoons NH_4^+ + OH^-,$$

and $\qquad K_b = \dfrac{(NH_4^+)(OH^-)}{(NH_4OH)} = 1.8 \times 10^{-5}$ at 25° C.

K_a is called the *acid constant*, and K_b the *basic constant*.

Example 15.5. Analysis of a solution of acetic acid, $HC_2H_3O_2$, at 25° C. showed the following concentrations:

$$(H^+) = (C_2H_3O_2^-) = 0.00150 \text{ mole per liter},$$
and $\qquad (HC_2H_3O_2) = 0.122 \text{ mole per liter}.$

Calculate K_a for acetic acid at 25° C.

Solution. From Sec. 15.3:

$$K_a = \frac{(H^+)(C_2H_3O_2^-)}{(HC_2H_3O_2)} = \frac{(0.00150)(0.00150)}{(0.122)} = 1.84 \times 10^{-5} \text{ at 25° C.}$$

Example 15.6. At 25° C. acetic acid, $HC_2H_3O_2$, is 1.34 per cent ionized in 0.100M solution. Calculate K_a.

Solution. In one liter of 1.00M $HC_2H_3O_2$ there would be one mole. Therefore, in 0.100M $HC_2H_3O_2$ which is 1.34 per cent ionized:

$$(H^+) = (C_2H_3O_2^-) = 0.100 \times 0.0134 = 0.00134 \text{ mole per liter},$$
and $\qquad (HC_2H_3O_2) = 0.10000 - 0.00134 = 0.09866 \text{ mole per liter}.$

Note: the term *mole* is commonly used in place of *gram-ion*.

Then $\qquad K_a = \dfrac{(0.00134)(0.00134)}{(0.09866)} = 1.82 \times 10^{-5}$ at 25° C.

Example 15.7. Calculate the hydrogen ion concentration in moles per liter, (H^+), of 1.000M acetic acid.

Solution. From Sec. 15.3 we see that K_a for acetic acid is equal to 1.84×10^{-5}.

Let $\qquad (H^+) = (C_2H_3O_2^-) = x$ mole per liter.

Then $\qquad (HC_2H_3O_2) = 1.000 - x$ mole per liter.

Substituting the above concentrations in the equilibrium expression for acetic acid, we have:

$$1.84 \times 10^{-5} = \frac{(x)(x)}{(1.000 - x)},$$

or $\qquad x^2 + 0.0000184x - 0.0000184 = 0.$

Solving for x gives (Sec. 3.13):

$$x = 4.29 \times 10^{-2} \text{ mole of } H^+ \text{ per liter.}$$

Problems

15.10. An acid dissociates according to the equation $HA \rightleftharpoons H^+ + A^-$. A one-molar solution of the acid is 1 per cent ionized. What is the value of K_a? *Ans.* 0.0001.

15.11. An acid dissociates according to the equation $H_2A \rightleftharpoons 2\,H^+ + A^-$. A 0.100M solution of the acid is 1 per cent ionized. What is the value of K_a? *Ans.* 1.0×10^{-8}.

15.12. The ionization of a one-molar solution of HCN is 0.010 per cent at 18° C. Calculate K_a. *Ans.* 1.0×10^{-8}.

15.13. Calculate the hydrogen ion concentration in moles per liter of a 0.010M solution of acetic acid at 25° C. *Ans.* 4.2×10^{-4}.

15.14. Calculate the value of K_a for a 0.010M solution of acetic acid, 4.2 per cent ionized, at 25° C. *Ans.* 1.8×10^{-5}.

15.15. Calculate the value of K_a for a 0.0010M solution of acetic acid which is 12.6 per cent ionized. *Ans.* 1.8×10^{-5}.

15.16. A 0.10M solution of ammonium hydroxide is 1.3 per cent ionized at 25° C. What is the value of K_b? *Ans.* 1.8×10^{-5}.

15.17. A one-molar solution of HCl is about 92 per cent ionized at room temperature. Calculate K_a for HCl. *Ans.* 10.6.

15.18. Calculate (OH^-) of 0.10M NH_4OH. *Ans.* 1.3×10^{-3} mole per liter.

15.4. The pH and pOH Values of Water Solutions. The ionic dissociation of water may be represented by the equilibrium:

$$H_2O \rightleftharpoons H^+ + OH^-.$$

Applying the equilibrium constant principle gives:

$$K_1 = \frac{(H^+)(OH^-)}{(H_2O)}.$$

K_1 is known as the *ionization constant* for water.

It has been shown experimentally that, at room temperature, 10,000,000 liters of water contain one mole of H^+, 1.008 g., and 10,000,000 liters of water contain one mole of OH^-, 17.008 g.

Therefore:

$$(H^+) = (OH^-) = \frac{1}{10,000,000} = 10^{-7} \text{ mole per liter in water.}$$

A quantity called the *ion product*, K_w, for water is given as:

$$K_w = (H^+)(OH^-) = 10^{-7} \times 10^{-7} = 10^{-14} \text{ at } 20° \text{ C.}$$

Since K_w is constant at any given temperature, in any water solution the product of the concentration of the H^+ and OH^- ions must be 10^{-14} at 20° C. when concentration is expressed as moles per liter. The addition of an acid to water will increase the hydrogen ion concentration; the addition of a base will increase the hydroxyl ion concentration. The increase in either case will be accompanied by a corresponding decrease in the other ion such that K_w is maintained constant. It is evident that in an acid solution the H^+ ion concentration is greater than 10^{-7} mole per liter, and in a solution of a base the H^+ ion concentration is less than 10^{-7} mole per liter.

Concentrations of H^+ and OH^- ions as expressed above are somewhat cumbersome to handle. Because of this, a system has been devised in which the acidity or alkalinity of solutions may be expressed as pH or pOH values. Table 15.1 shows the relationship among the quantities pH, pOH, (H^+), and (OH^-).

TABLE 15.1

METHODS OF EXPRESSING HYDROGEN ION AND HYDROXYL
ION CONCENTRATIONS

(H^+)	pH	(OH^-)	pOH
10^0	0	10^{-14}	14
10^{-1}	1	10^{-13}	13
10^{-2}	2	10^{-12}	12
10^{-3}	3	10^{-11}	11
10^{-7}	7	10^{-7}	7
10^{-12}	12	10^{-2}	2
10^{-13}	13	10^{-1}	1
10^{-14}	14	10^0	0

In Table 15.1 observe that pH + pOH = 14.

pH is defined as the logarithm of the reciprocal of the hydrogen ion concentration, (H$^+$). That is:

$$pH = \log \frac{1}{(H^+)}.$$

Example 15.8. Calculate the pH and pOH of a water solution containing 1.0×10^{-6} mole of H$^+$ ion per liter at 20° C.

Solution. Substituting the concentration of the hydrogen ion in the above formula gives:

$$pH = \log \frac{1}{1.0 \times 10^{-6}} = \log \frac{1}{0.000001} = \log 1{,}000{,}000 = 6.$$

Since pH + pOH = 14 at 20° C., then:

$$pOH = 14 - 6 = 8.$$

pH may be defined as the logarithm of the number of liters of solution containing one mole of H$^+$ ion.

Example 15.9. Calculate the pH of a water solution containing 1.0×10^{-6} mole of H$^+$ ion per liter at 20° C.

Solution. This problem is identical with Example 15.8.

Given that $1.0 \times 10^{-6} = 0.000001$ mole of H$^+$ ion is contained in 1.0 liter of water, then 1.0 mole of H$^+$ ion would be contained in $\dfrac{1}{0.000001}$ = 1,000,000 liters of water. Therefore:

$$pH = \log 1{,}000{,}000 = 6.$$

Observe that the above solution is essentially the same as that given for Example 15.8.

Problems

15.19. Following three successive additions of HCl to water, the respective hydrogen ion concentrations were 10^{-6}, $10^{-4.8}$, and $10^{-1.65}$. Calculate: (a) the concentration of the hydroxyl ion, (b) the pH, and (c) the pOH of each of the solutions. *Ans.* (a) 10^{-8}, $10^{-9.2}$, $10^{-12.35}$; (b) 6, 4.8, 1.65; (c) 8, 9.2, 12.35.

15.20. Following three successive additions of NaOH to water, the respective hydroxyl ion concentrations were 10^{-4}, $10^{-2.15}$, and $10^{-0.364}$. Calculate (a) the concentration of the hydrogen ion, (b) the pH, and (c) the pOH of each of the solutions. *Ans.* (a) 10^{-10}, $10^{-13.85}$, $10^{-13.636}$; (b) 10, 13.85, 13.636; (c) 4, 2.15, 0.364.

15.21. The concentration of hydrogen ion in a solution is 0.001 mole per liter. Calculate: (a) the grams of hydrogen ion per liter, (b) the liters of solution containing one mole of hydrogen ion, and (c) the pH and pOH values.   *Ans.* (a) 0.001008 g., (b) 1000 l., (c) 3, 11.

15.22. Calculate the pH value of 0.100M HCl, assuming complete ionization.
Ans. 1.

15.23. Calculate the pOH value of 0.100M NaOH, assuming complete ionization.   *Ans.* 1.

15.24. Calculate the pH and pOH of 0.30M HCl which is 88 per cent ionized.   *Ans.* 0.6, 13.4.

15.25. Calculate the concentration of hydrogen ion in moles per liter of a water solution having a pH of 4.5.   *Ans.* 3.2×10^{-5}.

15.26. A solution has a hydrogen ion concentration of 2.5×10^{-4} mole per liter. Calculate the pH of the solution.   *Ans.* 3.6.

15.27. Calculate the pH, (OH^-), and (H^+) of 0.001M KOH, assuming complete ionization.   *Ans.* 11, 10^{-3}, 10^{-11}.

15.28. Calculate the pH, (OH^-), and (H^+) of 0.001M HCl, assuming complete ionization.   *Ans.* 3, 10^{-11}, 10^{-3}.

15.29. Calculate the hydroxyl ion concentration in moles per liter of a solution (a) the pH of which is 4.0, and (b) the pOH of which is 4.0.
Ans. 10^{-10}, 10^{-4}.

15.5. The Solubility Product Principle. The *solubility product principle* applies to saturated solutions of very slightly soluble electrolytes. Such electrolytes may be assumed to be 100 per cent ionized in solution, the ions being in equilibrium with the undissolved solid according to the equation:

$$BaSO_4 \rightleftharpoons \underbrace{Ba^{+2} + SO_4^{-2}}_{\text{ions in solution}} \; .$$
$$\text{solid}$$

The equilibrium constant expression for the above equation would be:

$$K = \frac{(Ba^{+2})(SO_4^{-2})}{(BaSO_4)} \; .$$

Since the concentration of an undissolved solid such as $BaSO_4$ is unity, the above expression becomes:

$$K_{S.P.} = (Ba^{+2})(SO_4^{-2}),$$

where $K_{S.P.}$ is called the *solubility product constant*. The solubility product is therefore the product of the concentrations of the ions originating from a salt. Evidently, if the product of the concentrations of the ions is less than $K_{S.P.}$, the solution is unsaturated. If two solutions are mixed, one of which contains Ba^{+2} ions and the other SO_4^{-2} ions, precipitation of $BaSO_4$ will occur only if $(Ba^{+2})(SO_4^{-2}) > K_{S.P.}$ for $BaSO_4$.

$$K_{S.P.} = (Ba^{+2})(SO_4^{-2}) = 1.0 \times 10^{-10} \text{ at } 18° \text{ C.}$$

$K_{S.P.}$ varies with temperature, most values being given for room temperature, about 20° C.

Example 15.10. A solution of AgCl in equilibrium with the solid contained 1.3×10^{-5} mole of Ag^+ ion per liter and 1.3×10^{-5} mole of Cl^- ion per liter. Calculate $K_{S.P.}$ for AgCl.

Solution.

$$K_{S.P.} = (Ag^+)(Cl^-) = (1.3 \times 10^{-5})(1.3 \times 10^{-5}) = 1.7 \times 10^{-10}.$$

Example 15.11. The solubility of BaSO$_4$ in water at 18° C. is 0.00233 g. per liter. Calculate $K_{S.P.}$ for BaSO$_4$.

Solution. The concentrations of the Ba^{+2} and SO_4^{-2} ions must be found. Since 1 mole of barium sulfate yields 1 mole each of the two ions, then:

$$(Ba^{+2}) = (SO_4^{-2}) = (BaSO_4) = \frac{0.00233 \text{ g. BaSO}_4}{233 \frac{\text{g. BaSO}_4}{\text{mole}}} = 0.00001 \text{ mole.}$$

Therefore:

$K_{S.P.} = (0.00001)(0.00001) = 1.0 \times 10^{-10}$. Solubility product for BaSO$_4$.

Example 15.12. The solubility of Mg(OH)$_2$ in water at 18° C. is 0.00912 g. per liter. Calculate $K_{S.P.}$ for Mg(OH)$_2$, assuming complete ionization.

Solution. Mg(OH)$_2$ ionizes according to the equation:

$$Mg(OH)_2 \rightleftharpoons Mg^{+2} + \underbrace{OH^- + OH^-}.$$

1 mole   1 mole   2 moles

Therefore:

$$K_{S.P.} = (Mg^{+2})(OH^-)(OH^-) = (Mg^{+2})(OH^-)^2.$$

And   concentration of Mg(OH)$_2$ = $\dfrac{0.00912 \text{ g.}}{58.3 \frac{\text{g.}}{\text{mole}}}$ = 0.000156 mole per liter.

Since one mole of Mg(OH)$_2$ yields one mole of Mg^{+2} ion and two moles of OH^- ion, then:

$$(Mg^{+2}) = 0.000156 \text{ mole per liter,}$$

and $(OH^-) = 2 \times 0.000156 = 0.000312$ mole per liter.

Substituting the above values in the expression for $K_{S.P.}$ gives:

$$K_{S.P.} = (0.000156)(0.000312)^2 = 1.52 \times 10^{-11} \text{ for Mg(OH)}_2.$$

Example 15.13. One liter of solution was prepared containing 0.00408 mole of Pb(NO$_3$)$_2$. To this solution was added 0.0105 mole of NH$_4$Cl. Given that $K_{S.P.}$ for PbCl$_2$ is equal to 2.4×10^{-4} at room temperature, determine whether or not PbCl$_2$ will precipitate from the solution.

Solution. If the ionic product as given by the expression

$$K_{S.P.} = (Pb^{+2})(Cl^-)^2$$

is greater than 2.4×10^{-4}, precipitation of $PbCl_2$ will occur.

Since one mole of $Pb(NO_3)_2$ yields one mole of Pb^{+2} ion and one mole of NH_4Cl yields one mole of Cl^- ion, then:

$$(Pb^{+2}) = 0.00408 \text{ mole per liter,}$$
and $\qquad (Cl^-) = 0.0105$ mole per liter.

Therefore, $(Pb^{+2})(Cl^-)^2 = (0.00408)(0.0105)^2 = 4.5 \times 10^{-7}$.

Since 4.5×10^{-7} is less than 2.4×10^{-4}, the value of $K_{S.P.}$ for $PbCl_2$, precipitation of $PbCl_2$ will not occur.

Example 15.14. Given that $K_{S.P.}$ for $Al(OH)_3$ is equal to 3.7×10^{-15} at room temperature, calculate the solubility of $Al(OH)_3$ in grams per liter.

Solution. From the equation:

$$Al(OH)_3 \rightleftharpoons Al^{+3} + 3\ OH^-$$
$$\text{1 mole} \quad \text{1 mole} \quad \text{3 moles}$$

we have that:

$$K_{S.P.} = (Al^{+3})(OH^-)^3 = 3.7 \times 10^{-15}.$$

Let $\qquad\qquad x$ = moles of $Al(OH)_3$ dissolved per liter.

Then $\qquad\qquad x$ = moles of Al^{+3} ion per liter,

and $\qquad\qquad 3x$ = moles of OH^- ion per liter.

That is, $\qquad (x)(3x)^3 = 3.7 \times 10^{-15}$

or $\qquad\qquad x = 1.1 \times 10^{-4}$ moles of $Al(OH)_3$ per liter.

Since one mole of $Al(OH)_3$ is equal to 78 g.,
then $\quad 1.1 \times 10^{-4}$ mole of $Al(OH)_3 = (1.1 \times 10^{-4})(78) = 8.6 \times 10^{-3}$ g.

That is, the solubility of $Al(OH)_3$ is 8.6×10^{-3} gram per liter.

Example 15.15. What must be the concentration of Ag^+ ion in a solution containing 2.0×10^{-6} mole of Cl^- ion per liter to just start precipitation of $AgCl$, given that $K_{S.P.}$ for $AgCl$ is equal to 1.7×10^{-10}?

Solution. In a saturated solution of $AgCl$:

$$(Ag^+)(Cl^-) = 1.7 \times 10^{-10}$$

or $\qquad\qquad (Ag^+) = \dfrac{1.7 \times 10^{-10}}{(Cl^-)}$

and $\qquad\qquad (Ag^+) = \dfrac{1.7 \times 10^{-10}}{2.0 \times 10^{-6}} = 8.5 \times 10^{-5}$ mole per liter.

The solubility-product involves the use of very small quantities. However, such quantities are quite significant and find wide application in qualitative and quantitative analysis.

Problems

15.30. How many grams are there in 4.0×10^{-7} mole of Ag^+?

Ans. 4.3×10^{-5} g.

15.31. How many moles are there in 6.4×10^{-6} g. of S^{-2}?

Ans. 2.0×10^{-7} mole.

15.32. At room temperature the solubility of AgCl is 1.8×10^{-3} gram per liter. Calculate $K_{S.P.}$ for AgCl, assuming complete ionization.

Ans. 1.6×10^{-10}.

15.33. The solubility of ZnS at $25°$ C. is 3.5×10^{-12} mole per liter. Calculate $K_{S.P.}$ for ZnS.   *Ans.* 1.2×10^{-23}.

15.34. $K_{S.P.}$ for CaC_2O_4 is equal to 2.6×10^{-9}. Will CaC_2O_4 precipitate from 100 ml. of a solution containing 100 mg. of Ca^{+2} ion, to which has been added 0.02 mole of $(NH_4)_2C_2O_4$?   *Ans.* Yes.

15.35. $K_{S.P.}$ for ZnS is 1.2×10^{-23}. Calculate the S^{-2} ion concentration necessary to just start precipitation of ZnS from a 0.005M solution of $ZnSO_4$.   *Ans.* 2.4×10^{-21}.

15.36. $K_{S.P.}$ for $CaSO_4$ is equal to 6.1×10^{-5}. How many grams of $CaCl_2$ must be added to 500 ml. of 0.01M H_2SO_4 to just start precipitation of $CaSO_4$?   *Ans.* 0.34 g.

15.37. A solution in equilibrium with solid Ag_2S was found to contain 1.8×10^{-16} mole of S^{-2} ion per liter and 1.5×10^{-18} mole of Ag^+ ion per liter. Calculate $K_{S.P.}$ for Ag_2S.   *Ans.* 4.1×10^{-52}.

15.38. A solution in equilibrium with solid Bi_2S_3 contained 9.6×10^{-20} mole of Bi^{+3} ion per liter and 2.5×10^{-12} mole of S^{-2} ion per liter. Calculate $K_{S.P.}$ for Bi_2S_3.   *Ans.* 1.4×10^{-73}.

15.39. A saturated solution of Ag_2CrO_4 was prepared by shaking the pure compound with water. How much of the salt would dissolve in 500 ml. of water, given that $K_{S.P.}$ for Ag_2CrO_4 is 9.0×10^{-12}?

Ans. 0.022 g.

15.40. How many milligrams of $C_2O_4^{-2}$ ion must be present in 100 ml. of solution containing 0.050 mg. of Ba^{+2} ion in order to just start precipitation of BaC_2O_4, given that $K_{S.P.}$ for BaC_2O_4 is 1.5×10^{-7}?

Ans. 363 mg.

15.41. $K_{S.P.}$ for AgCl is equal to 1.7×10^{-10}. How many grams of AgCl will dissolve in one liter of 0.001M KCl, assuming the KCl to be completely ionized?   *Ans.* 2.4×10^{-5} g.

Equivalents in Solutions

15.6. The Gram-equivalent Weights of Acids and Bases. The gram-equivalent weight concept (Sec. 9.2) may be applied to compounds. Neutralization equations will be used to extend the concept to acids and bases.

$$NaOH + HCl \rightarrow NaCl + H_2O$$

1 mole	1 mole
1 g.-eq.-wt.	1 g.-eq.-wt.

$$2NaOH + H_2SO_4 \rightarrow Na_2SO_4 + 2H_2O$$

2 moles	1 mole
2 g.-eq.-wt.	2 g.-eq.-wt.

$$3NaOH + H_3PO_4 \rightarrow Na_3PO_4 + 3H_2O$$

3 moles	1 mole
3 g.-eq.-wt.	3 g.-eq.-wt.

$$Ca(OH)_2 + 2HCl \rightarrow CaCl_2 + 2H_2O$$

1 mole	2 moles
2 g.-eq.-wt.	2 g.-eq.-wt.

The fundamental reaction of neutralization is:

$$H^+ + OH^- \rightarrow H_2O.$$

One gram-equivalent weight of an acid contains one gram-atom of ionizable hydrogen, and one gram-equivalent weight of a base produces one mole of OH^- ion in solution. From the above equations we see that one gram-equivalent weight of an acid will neutralize one gram-equivalent weight of a base. The gram-equivalent weights of acids and bases may be calculated from the following rule: one gram-equivalent weight of an acid is equal to the molecular weight divided by the number of ionizable hydrogen atoms in a molecule, and one gram-equivalent weight of a base is equal to the formula weight divided by the number of ionizable hydroxyl radicals represented in the formula. For example, from the preceding equations we have that:

$$1.00 \text{ gram-equivalent weight of} \begin{cases} HCl & = 36.465 \div 1 = 36.465 \text{ g.} \\ H_2SO_4 & = 98.082 \div 2 = 49.041 \text{ g.} \\ H_3PO_4 & = 98.00 \div 3 = 32.7 \text{ g.} \\ NaOH & = 40.005 \div 1 = 40.005 \text{ g.} \\ Ca(OH)_2 & = 74.10 \div 2 = 37.05 \text{ g} \end{cases}$$

15.7. The Strengths of Solutions Expressed as Normality. *Normality*, N, is defined as the number of gram-equivalent weights of a substance in one liter of solution. This may be expressed in the form of an equation.

$$\text{Normality (N)} = \frac{\text{gram-equivalent weights (E)}}{\text{liters of solution (V)}}.$$

Example 15.16. Sufficient water was added to 100 g. of NaOH to make one liter of solution. What was the normality of the solution?

Solution. In the formula $N = \dfrac{E}{V}$:

$$N = x; \quad E = \frac{100 \text{ g.}}{40 \dfrac{\text{g.}}{\text{g.-eq.-wt.}}} = 2.5 \text{ gram-equivalent weights,}$$

and $V = 1.0$ liter. Therefore:

$$N = \frac{2.5 \text{ g.-eq.-wt.}}{1.0 \text{ l.}} = 2.5. \quad \text{The normality of the solution.}$$

Example 15.17. How much $Ca(OH)_2$ must be dissolved in water to prepare five liters of 0.050N solution?

Solution. $N = 0.050$; $E = x$; and $V = 5.0$. Therefore:

$$E = NV = (0.050)(5) = 0.25 \text{ gram-equivalent of } Ca(OH)_2.$$

Since 37.05 g. $Ca(OH)_2$ = one gram-equivalent weight,

then $37.05 \times 0.25 = 9.263$ g. $Ca(OH)_2$ is needed to prepare the solution.

Example 15.18. What is the normality of a solution containing 35.0 g. of KOH dissolved in sufficient water to make 400 ml. of solution?

Solution. $N = x$; $E = 35.0 \div 56.10 = 0.624$; and $V = 0.400$.

Therefore, $N = \dfrac{0.624}{0.400} = 1.56$. The normality of the solution.

15.8. The Titration of Acids and Bases. Titration is the process of determining the volume of a standard solution required to react with a known amount of the substance being analyzed.

In the titration of acids and bases, their normalities may be expressed as:

$$N_A = \frac{E_A}{V_A}, \quad \text{and} \quad N_B = \frac{E_B}{V_B}$$

or

$$E_A = N_A V_A, \quad \text{and} \quad E_B = N_B V_B.$$

At the end point of a titration $E_A = E_B$. Therefore:

$$N_A V_A = N_B V_B.$$

volume of base used
normality of base
volume of acid used
normality of acid

When V is given in liters in the above equation, the product NV represents gram-equivalent weights of the reactant; when V is given in milliliters, the product NV represents milliequivalent weights of the reactant.

Example 15.19. In a titration experiment 23.05 ml. of 0.100N NaOH was required to neutralize 10.00 ml. of a solution of H_2SO_4 of unknown strength. What was the normality of the acid solution?

Solution. From the relationship $N_A V_A = N_B V_B$ we have:

$$N_A = \frac{N_B V_B}{V_A} = \frac{(0.100)(23.05)}{(10.00)} = 0.231. \text{ Normality of the } H_2SO_4.$$

Example 15.20. A solution containing 0.275 g. of NaOH required 35.4 ml. of HCl for neutralization. What was the normality of the HCl?

Solution. One gram-equivalent weight of NaOH = 40.0 g.

Therefore, 0.275 g. NaOH $= \dfrac{0.275}{40.0} \times 1000 = 6.88$ milliequivalents.

Since $N_A V_A = N_B V_B =$ milliequivalents when V is measured in milliliters (Sec. 15.8), then:

$$35.4\, x = 6.88$$

or $x = 0.194.$ Normality of the HCl solution.

Example 15.21. What volume 0.250N acid would be required to react with 0.500 g. of $Ca(OH)_2$?

Solution.

$$0.500 \text{ g. } Ca(OH)_2 = \frac{0.500}{37.05} \times 1000 = 13.5 \text{ milliequivalents.}$$

Since $N_A V_A = N_B V_B,$
then $0.250x = 13.5$
or $x = 54.0$ ml. Volume of acid required.

Example 15.22. What would be the normality of a solution prepared by diluting 250 ml. of 0.400N H_2SO_4 with 1000 ml. of water?

Solution. The same number of milliequivalents must be in the diluted solution as in the original solution. That is:

$$N_1 V_1 = N_2 V_2.$$

Therefore, $(0.400N)(250 \text{ ml.}) = (xN)(1250 \text{ ml.})$
or $x = 0.080.$ Normality of diluted solution.

Example 15.23. A 0.311 g. sample of crude NaOH, when dissolved in water, required 46.1 ml. of 0.122N H_2SO_4 to neutralize the NaOH in the sample. Calculate the per cent of NaOH in the sample.

Solution. First calculate the number of grams of NaOH in the 0.311 g. sample. Then:

$$(0.122N)(46.1 \text{ ml.}) = 5.62 \text{ milliequivalents of NaOH.}$$

Since   1.00 milliequivalent of NaOH = 0.0400 g.,

then   5.62 milliequivalents of NaOH = 0.0400 × 5.62 = 0.225 g.

The per cent of NaOH in the sample would be:

$$\frac{0.225 \text{ g. NaOH}}{0.311 \text{ g. sample}} \times 100 = 72.3 \text{ per cent NaOH.}$$

Problems

15.42. How many grams each of H_3PO_4 and $Ca(OH)_2$ would be required to prepare 250 ml. of 0.100N solution?   *Ans.* 0.82 g., 0.93 g.

15.43. Make a table showing the number of grams of each of the following compounds required to make one liter of 1.0M, 1.0N, 2.0N, and 3.0N solutions: NaOH, $Ca(OH)_2$, $Al(OH)_3$, HCl, H_2SO_4, and H_3PO_4.

15.44. Calculate in terms of normality and molarity the strength of a solution containing 275 g. of KOH in 800 ml. of solution.

Ans. 6.13N, 6.13M.

15.45. How many milliliters of 0.50N solution could be prepared from 50.0 g. of NaOH?   *Ans.* 2500 ml.

15.46. What volume of H_2SO_4, density 1.84 g. per ml. and containing 98 per cent acid by weight, would be required to prepare one liter of 6N acid?   *Ans.* 164 ml.

15.47. Concentrated HCl has a density of 1.20 g. per ml. and is 39 per cent acid by weight. What is its normality?   *Ans.* 12.8N.

15.48. Concentrated NH_4OH has a density of 0.90 g. per ml. and is 28 per cent NH_3 by weight. What is its normality?   *Ans.* 15N.

15.49. Water was added to 25.0 ml. of 98 per cent H_2SO_4, density 1.84 g. per ml., to make 100 ml. of solution. Calculate the normality and molarity of the solution.   *Ans.* 9.20N, 4.60M.

15.50. In a titration, 32.8 ml. of 0.255N H_2SO_4 was required to neutralize 42.3 ml. of a solution of NaOH of unknown strength. Calculate (a) the normality of the NaOH solution, and (b) the grams of Na_2SO_4 formed.   *Ans.* 0.198N, 0.594 g.

15.51. What volume of 1.75N KOH solution, diluted to one liter, would give a 1.00N solution of KOH?   *Ans.* 571 ml.

15.52. A 2.34 g. sample of impure H_2SO_4 required 42.3 ml. of 0.100N NaOH to neutralize the acid in the sample. What was the per cent purity of the impure acid?   *Ans.* 8.86%.

15.53. How many grams of zinc would be dissolved by the action of one liter of 1.00N HCl?   *Ans.* 32.69 g.

15.54. A 10.00 ml. sample of vinegar, density 1.01 g. per ml., was diluted to 100 ml. volume. It was found that 25.0 ml. of the diluted vinegar required 24.15 ml. of 0.0976N NaOH to neutralize it. Calculate the strength of the vinegar in terms of (a) normality, (b) grams of $HC_2H_3O_2$ per liter, and (c) per cent $HC_2H_3O_2$ in the vinegar.

Ans. 0.943N, 56.6 g., 5.60%.

15.55. How many liters of CO_2, measured at standard conditions, would be liberated by the action of 1500 ml. of 2N H_2SO_4 on $CaCO_3$?

Ans. 33.6 l.

15.56. How many milliliters of 6N HCl would be required to react with 1.45 g. of Mg? *Ans.* 20 ml.

15.57. An experiment calls for 300 ml. of 1.00N HCl. The only acid available is 6.0N HCl. How much water and 6.0N HCl must be used?

Ans. 250 ml. water, 50 ml. acid.

15.58. It was found that 0.3031 g. of Mg required 27.40 ml. of 0.910N HCl to react to form $MgCl_2$. Calculate the atomic weight of magnesium, knowing that it is approximately 25. *Ans.* 24.32.

15.59. How many grams of NaCl would be formed by mixing 50.0 ml. of 1.54N HCl with 50.0 ml. of 1.12N NaOH? *Ans.* 3.27 g.

15.60. Commercial lye is principally NaOH. A 0.564 g. sample of lye required 41.6 ml. of 0.251N H_2SO_4 to neutralize the NaOH it contained. Calculate the per cent of NaOH in the lye. *Ans.* 74.1%.

16

Reactions Involving Oxidation and Reduction

Oxidation and reduction type of reactions are so important that special consideration is given them in this chapter. However, all the principles applying to other types of reactions apply also to oxidation-reduction reactions. These are the reactions commonly occurring in nature, such as in plant and animal tissue. The concept of normality, as presented in Chapter 15, is applied to oxidants and reductants in solution.

Methods of Expressing Strengths of Oxidizing and Reducing Solutions

16.1. Introduction. *Oxidation-reduction reactions* are those in which some of the atoms undergo a change in oxidation state. That is, there is an exchange of electrons among the atoms. For example:

$$\overset{(0)}{2\,Na} + \overset{(0)}{Cl_2} \rightarrow \overset{(+1)(-1)}{2\,NaCl}.$$

$$\overset{(0)}{Cu} + \overset{(0)}{Cl_2} \rightarrow \overset{(+2)(-1)}{CuCl_2}.$$

$$\overset{(+1)(-2)}{H_2S} + \overset{(0)}{Cl_2} \rightarrow \overset{(+1)(-1)}{2\,HCl} + \overset{(0)}{S}.$$

In an equation the total gain in oxidation number of the atoms must be equal to the loss in oxidation number. For example:

$$
\begin{array}{c}
\overbrace{}^{(2)(-1)\,=\,-2} \\
H_2S + Cl_2 \quad \rightarrow \quad 2\,HCl + S \\
\underbrace{}_{+2}
\end{array}
$$

$$
\begin{array}{c}
\overbrace{}^{(2)(-5)\,=\,-10} \\
2\,KMnO_4 + 16\,HCl \rightarrow 2\,KCl + 2\,MnCl_2 + 8\,H_2O + 5\,Cl_2 \\
\underbrace{}_{(10)(+1)\,=\,+10}
\end{array}
$$

16.2. Solutions of Oxidants and Reductants Expressed in Terms of Normality.   The concept of normality may be applied to solutions of oxidizing and reducing agents (Sec. 15.7).   As with acids and bases, the normality of an oxidizing or reducing agent is defined as the number of gram-equivalent weights per liter of solution.   That is, $N = \dfrac{E}{V}$.   One gram-equivalent weight of an oxidant or reductant is equal to the formula weight divided by the change in oxidation number of the atoms expressed by the formula.   For example:

$$\begin{array}{cc} (+2) & (+3) \\ 2\,FeCl_2 + Cl_2 \rightarrow 2\,FeCl_3. \end{array}$$

Then   1.00 gram-equivalent weight of $FeCl_2 = \dfrac{126.76}{1} = 126.76$ g.

In the reaction involving $KMnO_4$ in Sec. 16.1:

1.00 gram-equivalent weight of $KMnO_4 = \dfrac{158.03}{5} = 31.61$ g.,

and in the reaction:

$$\begin{array}{l} (+7) \qquad\qquad\qquad\qquad\qquad\qquad\qquad\qquad\qquad (+4) \\ KMnO_4 + NaOH + FeSO_4 \rightarrow K_2SO_4 + Na_2SO_4 + Fe_2(SO_4)_3 + MnO_2 + H_2O, \end{array}$$

1.00 gram-equivalent weight of $KMnO_4 = \dfrac{158.03}{3} = 52.68$ g.

That is, the gram-equivalent weight of an oxidant or reductant is valid only when referred to a particular reaction.

Analyses Involving Oxidation and Reduction

16.3. Titration.   Solutions of oxidants and reductants are titrated in the same manner as are acids and bases (Sec. 15.8).

Example 16.1.   The following data were obtained in the titration of $KMnO_4$ and HCl solutions as given in Sec. 16.1:

> Volume of $KMnO_4$ solution used = 10.00 ml.
> Volume of 0.100N HCl used   = 17.20 ml.

Calculate (a) the normality of the $KMnO_4$ solution, and (b) the number of grams of $KMnO_4$ per liter of solution.

Solution.   (a)

$$N_{KMnO_4} = \frac{(0.100)(17.20)}{(10.00)} = 0.172.$$

(b) 1.00 gram-equivalent weight of $KMnO_4$ = 31.61 g. (Sec. 16.2).
Therefore,   1.00 liter of 0.172N $KMnO_4$ = 31.61 × 0.172 = 5.44 g.

Example 16.2. How many grams of $KMnO_4$ will react with 1.5 gram-equivalent weights of HCl according to the equation given in Sec. 16.1?

Solution. Equal gram-equivalent weights of oxidants and reductants react. Therefore, 1.5 gram-equivalent weights of $KMnO_4$ will react.

1.00 gram-equivalent weight of $KMnO_4$ = 31.61 g. Therefore:

1.50 gram-equivalent weights of $KMnO_4$ = 31.61 × 1.50 = 47.4 g.

Problems

16.1. Given the equation:

$K_2Cr_2O_7 + 7 H_2SO_4 + 6 FeSO_4 \rightarrow K_2SO_4 + Cr_2(SO_4)_3 + 3 Fe_2(SO_4)_3 + 7 H_2O$, calculate: (a) the number of grams in one gram-equivalent weight each of $FeSO_4$ and $K_2Cr_2O_7$, and (b) the number of grams required to prepare one liter of 0.500N $K_2Cr_2O_7$.   *Ans.* (a) 151.92 g., 49.04 g., (b) 24.52 g.

16.2. How much $K_2Cr_2O_7$ would be required to prepare 1500 ml. of 0.100N solution?   *Ans.* 7.35 g.

16.3. In a titration 61.33 ml. of 0.2N $K_2Cr_2O_7$ was required to react with 47.65 ml. of $FeSO_4$ solution. Calculate (a) the normality of the $FeSO_4$ solution, and (b) the number of grams of $K_2Cr_2O_7$ in one liter of the solution.   *Ans.* (a) 0.257N, (b) 9.81 g.

16.4. Calculate the gram-equivalent weight of iodine and hydrogen sulfide based upon the reaction:

$I_2 + H_2S \rightarrow 2 HI + S.$ *Ans.* 126.92 g., 17.04 g.

16 5. Iodine reacts with $Na_2S_2O_3$ according to the equation:

$I_2 + 2 Na_2S_2O_3 \rightarrow 2 NaI + Na_2S_4O_6.$

A 0.376 g. sample of crude iodine required 17.1 ml. of 0.100N $Na_2S_2O_3$ to react with the iodine in the sample. Calculate the per cent purity of the crude iodine.   *Ans.* 57.7%.

16.6. What are the gram-equivalent weights of the oxidants and reductants in each of the following reactions?

(a) $KClO_3 + H_2SO_4 + FeSO_4 \rightarrow Fe_2(SO_4)_3 + KCl + H_2O.$

(b) $KMnO_4 + HCl + FeCl_2 \rightarrow MnCl_2 + KCl + FeCl_3 + H_2O.$

    Ans. (a) $KClO_3$ = 20.43 g.
                   $FeSO_4$ = 151.92 g.
         (b) $KMnO_4$ = 31.61 g.
                   $FeCl_2$ = 126.76 g.

16.7. Using the data in problem 16.6, calculate the number of grams required to prepare:

(a) 1800 ml. of 0.125N $KClO_3$ solution.   *Ans.* 4.60 g.

(b) 800 ml. of 0.750N $FeSO_4$ solution.   *Ans.* 91.2 g.

(c) 1500 ml. of 0.100N $KMnO_4$ solution.   *Ans.* 4.74 g.

(d) 1800 ml. of 0.250N $FeCl_2$ solution.   *Ans.* 57.0 g.

16.8. How many grams of $KClO_3$ will react with 500 ml. of 12.0N HCl according to the equation:

$$KClO_3 + 6 HCl \rightarrow 3 H_2O + KCl + 3 Cl_2?$$ *Ans.* 122.5 g.

16.9. How many equivalents of $K_2Cr_2O_7$ will react with 50.0 g. of $FeSO_4$, according to the equation given in problem 16.1? *Ans.* 0.329.

16.10. How many grams of $KMnO_4$ would be required to oxidize 100 g. of $FeCl_2$, according to the equation given in problem 16.6?

Ans. 24.9 g.

17

Electrochemistry

The passage of an electric current through a solution brings about chemical changes which obey the laws and principles of chemical changes occurring in test tube reactions. First, electric terms are defined; there follows a discussion of the changes brought about in solution due to the passage of an electric current, and, conversely, the generation of an electric current by chemical change as in the lead storage battery and dry cell. As in previous discussions the quantitative aspects are stressed.

Units Associated with the Measurement of Electricity

17.1. Introduction. In many chemical reactions the energy is liberated in the form of electricity rather than heat. Such is the case in a dry cell or storage battery. Also, electric energy may be used to bring about chemical changes.

Electrochemistry involves the study of electric energy, either in its effect in bringing about a chemical change, or as a product of a chemical change.

17.2. Practical Units of Electricity. Certain arbitrary units have been established for the measurement of electric energy. Only the *practical units* of electricity will be discussed. One *faraday* of electricity is defined as the amount of electric energy required to liberate one gram-equivalent weight of an element from solution. A smaller unit of quantity, the *coulomb*, is defined as the quantity of electricity required to deposit 0.001118 g. of silver from a solution containing Ag^+ ions. Since:

1.00 gram-equivalent weight of silver = 107.88 g., then:

$$1.00 \text{ faraday} = \frac{107.88 \text{ g.}}{0.001118 \frac{\text{g.}}{\text{coulomb}}} = 96,490 \text{ coulombs.}$$

An *ampere* is a rate of flow of one coulomb per second. An *ohm* is the resistance of a column of mercury one square millimeter in cross section and 106.300 centimeters in length at 0° C. A *volt* is the potential necessary to drive a current of one ampere through a resistance of one ohm. Ohm's law expresses the relationship among the ampere, volt, and ohm:

$$\text{Amperes (I)} = \frac{\text{Volts (V)}}{\text{Ohms (R)}}$$

Laws Relating to Conduction in Solution

17.3. Faraday's Laws of Electrolysis. *Electrolysis* is the process resulting from the passage of an electric current through a solution of an electrolyte.

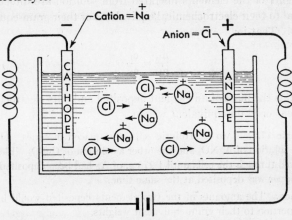

Fig. 17.1. Electric conduction in solutions of electrolytes.

Faraday stated two laws relating to electrolysis. The first law states that the amount of electrochemical change at an electrode is directly proportional to the quantity of electricity flowing through the solution. The number of grams of an element liberated by one coulomb is called the *electrochemical equivalent* of the element; the number of grams liberated by one faraday is called the *gram-equivalent weight* of the element (Sec. 17.2). Below is the mathematical statement of the first law:

m = eQ.

　　　quantity of electricity in coulombs
　　electrochemical equivalent in grams
weight in grams of substance liberated

When Q is expressed in faradays, then e becomes the gram-equivalent weight.

Example 17.1. A current of 0.050 ampere was allowed to pass through a solution of silver nitrate for 30 minutes. How much silver was deposited?

Solution. One coulomb will deposit 0.001118 g. of silver. A coulomb is one ampere per second. Since the current of 0.050 ampere flowed for $30 \times 60 = 1800$ seconds:

$$1800 \times 0.050 = 90 \text{ coulombs. Electric energy used.}$$

And $0.001118 \, \dfrac{\text{g.}}{\text{coulombs}} \times 90 \text{ coulombs} = 0.10$ g.   Silver deposited.

Faraday's second law states that, for a given quantity of electricity, the weights of the elements liberated from solution are directly proportional to their electrochemical equivalents or their gram-equivalent weights. That is:

$$\frac{m_1}{m_2} = \frac{e_1}{e_2},$$

where m is the mass of an element deposited and e its electrochemical equivalent or gram-equivalent weight.

Example 17.2. Two electrolytic cells were placed in series. One contained a solution of $AgNO_3$ and the other a solution of $CuSO_4$. Electricity was passed through the cells until 1.273 g. of Ag had been deposited. How much copper was deposited at the same time?

Solution. The amounts of the two elements deposited would be in direct proportion to their gram-equivalent weights.

Therefore: $\dfrac{1.273 \text{ g. Ag}}{x \text{ g. Cu}} = \dfrac{107.88 \text{ g. Ag}}{31.77 \text{ g. Cu}}$

or $x = 0.3749$ g. Cu deposited.

Example 17.3. How many grams each of Ag^+ and Cu^{+2} ions would be deposited by 0.040 faraday?

Solution. Since one faraday deposits one gram-equivalent weight of an element, then 0.040 faraday would deposite 0.040 gram-equivalent weight of an element. Therefore:

$$107.88 \times 0.040 = 4.3 \text{ g. of Ag deposited}$$
and $31.79 \times 0.040 \;\; = 1.3$ g. of Cu deposited.

Example 17.4. Calculate the atomic weight of calcium, given that 0.0324 faraday liberated 0.651 g. of the element. The approximate weight of calcium is 40.

Solution. The weight of an element deposited by one faraday is the gram-equivalent weight of the element. Therefore:

$$\frac{0.0324 \text{ faraday}}{0.651 \text{ g. Ca}} = \frac{1.00 \text{ faraday}}{x \text{ g. Ca}}$$

or $x = 20.1$ g.   Gram-equivalent weight of Ca.

Oxidation number of Ca $= \dfrac{40}{20.1} = 2$.   Therefore:

Atomic weight of Ca $= 20.1 \times 2 = 40.2$.

Example 17.5. It was found that 0.172 g. of chromium was deposited by 0.0761 ampere in 3 hours and 30 minutes. Calculate (a) the electrochemical equivalent of chromium, and (b) the gram-equivalent weight of chromium.

Solution. (a)

Coulombs used $= 12,600$ sec. $\times 0.0761$ amp. $= 959$.

By definition, one coulomb deposits one electrochemical equivalent of an element. Therefore:

0.172 g. $\div$ 959 coulombs $= 0.000179$ g. per coulomb.   Electrochemical
                                                                                              equivalent of chromium.

(b) By definition, one gram-equivalent weight or 96,490 electrochemical equivalents of chromium would be deposited from solution by one faraday. Therefore:

$0.000179 \dfrac{\text{g.}}{\text{coulomb}} \times 96,490 \text{ coulomb} = 17.3$.   Gram-equivalent weight of
                                                                                                                chromium.

17.4. The Significance of the Avogadro Number in Electrolysis.

In Sec. 8.4 it was shown that one gram-atom of an element contains N atoms, where N is the Avogadro number equal to 6.023×10^{23}. In Sec. 9.3 it was shown that one gram-equivalent weight of an element involves N electrons of that element when it enters into chemical combination with another element. Therefore, in the process of electrolysis N electrons pass through the solution for each faraday used. That is, one faraday contains 6.023×10^{23} electrons.

Problems

17.1. A given quantity of electricity was passed through each of two cells containing Cu^{+2} ions and Ag^+ ions, respectively. It was found that 0.637 g. of copper had been deposited in the one cell. How much silver was deposited in the other cell?   *Ans*. 2.16 g.

17.2. Calculate the quantities of ferrous and ferric ions that would be deposited by 1.000 faraday.   *Ans*. 27.9 g., 18.6 g.

17.3.   Calculate the quantities of chlorine, calcium, and aluminum that would be deposited by 1500 coulombs.

$Ans.$ 0.553 g., 0.312 g., 0.140 g.

17.4.   How much mercurous and mercuric mercury would be deposited by 0.100 ampere in 30 minutes? $Ans.$ 0.374 g., 0.187 g.

17.5.   How much would a copper plate increase in weight if silver-plated by a current of 650 milliamperes for 24 hours? $Ans.$ 62.8 g.

17.6.   It was found that 0.287 g. of nickel was deposited by a current of 175 milliamperes in 90 minutes.   Calculate (a) the electrochemical equivalent of nickel, (b) the gram-equivalent weight of nickel, and (c) the valence of nickel. $Ans.$ 0.000304 g., 29.33 g., 2.

17.7.   How much hydrogen at standard conditions would be deposited by a current of one ampere flowing for one minute? $Ans.$ 6.96 ml.

17.8.   Chlorine is prepared commercially by the electrolysis of a brine solution.   A current of 2500 amperes was passed through a brine solution for 24 hours.   Calculate (a) the volume of hydrogen liberated at S.C., (b) the volume of chlorine liberated at S.C., and (c) the amount of NaOH formed at the cathode.

$Ans.$ 2.5×10^4 l., 2.5×10^4 l., 89.6 kg.

17.9.   If a given quantity of electricity deposits 1.952 g. of platinic ion, how much auric ion would be deposited by the same amount of electricity? $Ans.$ 2.629 g.

17.10.   What current strength would be required to deposit 1.50 g. of silver per hour? $Ans.$ 0.373 ampere.

17.11.   A metal A forms the oxide AO.   A given quantity of electricity deposited 0.862 g. of silver and 0.321 g. of the metal A.   Calculate the atomic weight of the element A. $Ans.$ 80.4.

17.12.   What weight of water would be decomposed by a current of 100 amperes in 12 hours? $Ans.$ 403 g.

17.13.   A current of 1.46 amperes was found to liberate 203 ml. of chlorine at S.C. in 20 minutes.   What is the gram-equivalent weight of chlorine? $Ans.$ 35.5 g.

17.14.   How long must a current of one ampere flow through acidulated water in order to liberate one gram of hydrogen? $Ans.$ 26.8 hrs.

17.15.   How many ampere-hours would be required to deposit one gram-equivalent weight of an element? $Ans.$ 26.8.

17.16.   What weight of sodium would be deposited in one hour with a potential of 100 volts and a resistance of 50 ohms? $Ans.$ 1.72 g.

17.17.   How much each of Cu^+ and Cu^{+2} would be deposited as copper by a current of 0.25 ampere flowing for 60 minutes?

$Ans.$ 0.593 g., 0.297 g.

17.18.   How many molecules of chlorine would be deposited from a solution containing Cl^- ions in one minute by a current of 300 milliamperes?

$Ans.$ 5.6×10^{19}.

17.19. What volumes each of hydrogen and oxygen would be obtained at 27° C. and 740 mm. of Hg by passing a current of 25 amperes through acidulated water for 24 hours?   *Ans.* 284 l., 142 l.

17.20. How many electrons are there in one coulomb?   *Ans.* 6.2×10^{18}.

17.21. How many electrons are lost by one gram of Cl^- ion as the result of electrolysis?   *Ans.* 1.70×10^{22}.

17.22. How many electrons are gained by one gram of Cu^{+2} ion as the result of electrolysis?   *Ans.* 1.90×10^{22}.

17.23. What is the charge in coulombs on a S^{-2} ion?   *Ans.* 3.2×10^{-19}.

18

Nuclear Chemistry

Within recent years the scope of chemistry has been expanded to include changes which occur within the atom itself, and the energy associated with such changes. The discussion in this chapter will be limited to changes within the atom which have been taking place spontaneously during past ages, and changes within the atom brought about by the inventive genius of mankind.

Radioactivity

18.1. Introduction. Radioactivity involves the nuclei of atoms. The nuclei of certain isotopes are unstable, undergoing disintegration over which man has no control, whereas with stable isotopes no such process occurs. When nuclei undergo disintegration, two types of particles may be lost: (1) *alpha* (α) particles of atomic mass 4 and a +2 charge, and (2) *beta* (β) particles of negligible mass and a charge of -1. That is, when the nucleus of an atom loses an α-particle, its weight decreases by 4 atomic mass units, and the nuclear charge (atomic number) decreases by 2. When the nucleus of an atom loses a β-particle, there is no change in weight, and the nuclear charge increases by one. For example:

$$_{92}U^{238} \rightarrow {}_{90}Th^{234} \quad + \quad {}_{2}He^{4}.$$

| Uranium | Thorium | α-particle |

$$_{90}Th^{234} \rightarrow {}_{91}Pa^{234} \quad + \quad 1e^{-}.$$

| Thorium | Protactinium | β-particle |

18.2. Rate of Radioactive Disintegration. The products of disintegration of a naturally occurring radioactive substance appear always to be the same. Two important facts have been established concerning radioactive disintegration: (1) the number of nuclei disintegrating per unit of time for a given substance is directly proportional to the mass undergoing disintegration, and (2) each radioactive substance has a characteristic rate of disintegration.

124

The *half-life period* of a radioactive substance is the time required for one-half of a given mass of the substance to undergo disintegration. Half-life periods vary enormously with different substances, one product of uranium disintegration having a half-life period of 1.5×10^{-4} seconds and another a half-life period of 270,000 years.

Example 18.1. The half-life period of radon, $_{86}Rn^{222}$, is approximately 4 days. A tube containing 1.00 microgram (0.000001 g.) of radon was stored in a hospital clinic for 12 days. How much radon remained in the tube?

Solution. Every 4 days one-half the remaining radon would disintegrate. Then, according to the following scheme:

$$\text{days} \; - \; 0 \; - \; 4 \; - \; 8 \; - \; 12$$
$$\text{radon left} \; - \; 1.00 \; - \; 0.50 \; - \; 0.25 \; - \; 0.125 \text{ micrograms left.}$$

The Transmutation of Elements

18.3. Introduction. The development of artificial radioactivity has made possible the conversion of one element into another by means of nuclear changes within the atom. The bombardment of nuclei with certain high energy particles such as protons $(_1H^1)$, deuterons $(_1H^2)$, alpha particles $(_2H^4)$, beta particles (e^-), and neutrons $(_0n^1)$ may result in the capture of the particle by a nucleus, followed by elimination of a particle from the nucleus different from that captured. The result is the formation of unstable radioactive isotopes of the element, or transmutation into a new element.

18.4. Nuclear Reactions. Transmutation of elements and the artificial preparation of unstable radioactive isotopes involves nuclear changes within the atom. For example, when aluminum is bombarded with alpha particles, the products are radioactive phosphorus and neutrons.

$$_{13}Al^{27} + _2He^4 \rightarrow _{15}P^{30} + _0n^1.$$

When lithium is bombarded with deuterons the product is helium.

$$_3Li^6 + _1H^2 \rightarrow 2 \; _2He^4.$$

The bombardment of lithium 7 with deuterons produces a different type of reaction.

$$_3Li^7 + _1H^2 \rightarrow _4Be^6 + _0n^1.$$

Any process in which a nucleus reacts with another nucleus, or with the elementary particles previously mentioned, to produce new nuclei is called a *nuclear reaction*.

18.5. Energy of Nuclear Reactions. The number of protons and neutrons in the atoms of the elements is known. The mass of a proton is equal to 1.00758 atomic mass units, and the mass of a neutron to 1.00897 atomic mass units. Since a helium nucleus consists of two protons and two neutrons, its mass should be:

$$(2 \times 1.00758) + (2 \times 1.00897) = 4.0331 \text{ atomic mass units.}$$

Actually, the helium nucleus has been found to have a mass of 4.003 atomic mass units. The difference,

$$4.033 - 4.003 = 0.030 \text{ atomic mass units,}$$

represents the mass converted to energy in the process of formation of a helium nucleus. This process is probably occurring on the sun at the present time. The difference in nuclear weight is called the *mass defect* of the atom.

The amount of energy liberated may be calculated by means of the Einstein equation (Sec. 13.1). Then, for helium:

$$E = (2.2 \times 10^{13})(0.030) = 6.6 \times 10^{11} \text{ calories.}$$

That is, in the process of formation of 4.003 grams of helium from protons and neutrons, 6.6×10^{11} calories is liberated.

Problems

18.1. Diffusion methods are employed in the separation of U^{235} and U^{238} (Sec. 7.11). The fluorides, UF_6, of the two isotopes exist in the gaseous state above 56° C. at 760 mm. of Hg. What are the relative rates of diffusion of the two fluorides? *Ans.* 1.0043 : 1.0000.

18.2. Explain the nuclear changes necessary to bring about the following transmutations: (a) $_{13}Al^{27} \rightarrow {}_{15}P^{30}$, (b) $_3Li^7 \rightarrow {}_4Be^6$, and (c) $_{92}U^{238} \rightarrow {}_{90}Th^{234}$.

18.3. What is the percentage of radium in a pitchblende which yielded 25 mg. of $RaCl_2$ from 15 tons of ore? *Ans.* $(1.4 \times 10^{-7})\%$.

18.4. The market price of radium is about $50,000 per gram. What would be the cost of 50 micrograms of $RaCl_2$ based on radium content?
Ans. $1.90.

18.5. How much of a one-gram mass of a radioactive substance would remain after 30 days if its half-life period is 5 days?
Ans. 0.0156 g.

18.6. The half-life period of $_{15}P^{30}$ is about 3 minutes. How much of a 16-microgram sample would remain after 15 minutes?
Ans. 0.50 microgram.

18.7. The half-life period of radioactive carbon, C^{14}, is about 4700 years. How many years would be required to reduce 32 micrograms of the isotope to one microgram? *Ans.* 23,500 years.

18.8.   A radioactive isotope $_{11}A^{24}$ loses a β-particle, yielding a stable isotope B. What is the element B?   *Ans.* Mg.

18.9.   When $_{83}Bi^{209}$ is bombarded with α-particles, the bismuth nucleus captures one particle with the accompanying expulsion of two neutrons. What is the new element which is formed?   *Ans.* At.

18.10. When U^{238} is bombarded with neutrons, each nucleus captures one neutron. What isotope of uranium is formed?   *Ans.* U^{239}.

18.11. When N^{14} is bombarded with neutrons, the nitrogen nucleus captures a neutron with the formation of radioactive carbon, C^{14}. What particle is expelled from the nitrogen nucleus in order to bring about this transmutation?   *Ans.* A proton.

18.12. Calculate the mass defect for sodium.   *Ans.* 0.194.

18.13. Calculate the energy in calories released when one gram-atom of sodium is formed from neutrons and protons. *Ans.* 4.3×10^{12} cal.

18.14. Calculate the energy in calories released when one atom of beryllium is formed from neutrons and protons. *Ans.* 2.3×10^{-12} cal.

Appendixes

Appendixes

I. Graphical Presentation of Data

In Fig. 1, XX' and YY' are two straight lines meeting at right angles at O. YY' is called the *ordinate* and XX' the *abscissa*, the two being called the *co-ordinate axes*. The point O is called the *origin*. The X- and Y-axes divide the plane in which they are drawn into the four quadrants I, II, III, and IV.

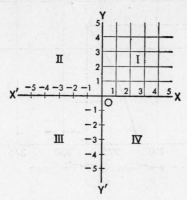

Fig. 1.   Co-ordinate axes.

Any point in the plane in Fig. 1 is located by its perpendicular distance to the X- and Y-axes. Distances measured to the right of the Y-axis and above the X-axis are considered positive; distances measured to the left of the Y-axis and below the X-axis are negative. For example, the point a, lying in quadrant I, is located by the values $X = 3$ and $Y = 2$.

Since X and Y values for any point lying in quadrant I are positive, this quadrant is most commonly used for making graphs.

Fig. 1. represents a two-dimensional graph using two variables. A three-dimensional graph involving three variables may be used in which the third axis, represented by ZZ', is drawn perpendicular to the paper at point 0 in Fig. 1.

Example 1. The following data give the number of grams of sugar that will dissolve in 100 grams of water at the given temperature.

Temperature, °C. —   0 — 20 — 40 — 60 — 80 — 100
Grams of sugar   — 179 — 204 — 238 — 287 — 362 — 487

Plot the above data and determine the solubility of sugar at 50°C.

Solution. Quadrant I will be used to plot the data as shown in Fig. 2.

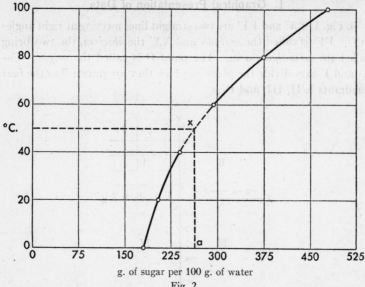

g. of sugar per 100 g. of water

Fig. 2.

Let each division on the X-axis represent 75 g. of sugar and each division on the Y-axis 20° C. The points are plotted and connected by means of a smooth curve as shown in the figure. A well-plotted graph will utilize approximately equal portions of the X- and Y-axes.

To find the solubility of sugar at 50° C., draw a line from the 50° C. point on the Y-axis parallel to the X-axis until it intersects the curve at x. Drop a line from this point parallel to the Y-axis until it intersects the X-axis at a. The point a corresponds to 260 g. of sugar. That is, 260 g. of sugar will dissolve in 100 g. of water at 50° C.

Problems

1. The following data give the solubility of ammonia in grams per 1000 grams of water at 760 mm. of Hg. Plot the data and determine the solubility of ammonia at 25° C. and at 100° C.

Temperature, °C. — 10 — 20 — 30 — 40 — 50 — 60 — 70 — 80
Grams of NH₃   — 720 — 525 — 395 — 300 — 235 — 190 — 155 — 130

2. Plot the data in Appendix II, giving the vapor pressure of water at temperatures of from 0° C. to 100° C. At what temperature would water boil on the top of Pikes Peak, Colorado, with the barometer reading 450 mm. of Hg?

3. Given 50 liters of hydrogen at 0° C. and 1.00 atmosphere, calculate the volume of the hydrogen at 2.00, 4.00, 6.00, 8.00, and 10.00 atmospheres, temperature constant. Plot the data.

II. The Vapor Pressure of Water in mm. of Hg at Temperatures of from 0° C. to 100° C.

Temp. °C.	Pressure	Temp. °C.	Pressure	Temp. °C.	Pressure
0	4.6	15	12.8	30	31.8
1	4.9	16	13.6	31	33.7
2	5.3	17	14.5	32	35.7
3	5.7	18	15.5	33	37.7
4	6.1	19	16.5	34	39.9
5	6.5	20	17.5	35	42.2
6	7.0	21	18.7	36	44.6
7	7.5	22	19.8	37	47.1
8	8.0	23	21.1	38	49.7
9	8.6	24	22.4	39	52.4
10	9.2	25	23.8	40	55.3
11	9.9	26	25.2	50	92.5
12	10.5	27	26.7	60	149.4
13	11.2	28	28.3	80	355.1
14	12.0	29	30.0	100	760.0

III. Logarithms

In the expression $a^x = y$, x is the logarithm of y to the base a, where a must be a positive number other than one. A *logarithm* is therefore an exponent and, as such, follows the rules applying to exponents (Secs. 3.5 to 3.12). The discussion which follows will be limited to the use of the base 10.

A logarithm is divided into two parts, the integer part called the *characteristic*, and the decimal fraction called the *mantissa*. Remember: the mantissa of a logarithm is always positive, whereas the characteristic may be either positive or negative. The following table shows some important principles relating to logarithms.

$$\log 635 \quad = \log (6.35 \times 10^2) \quad = \quad 2.80277$$
$$\log 63.5 \quad = \log (6.35 \times 10^1) \quad = \quad 1.80277$$
$$\log 6.35 \quad = \log (6.35 \times 10^0) \quad = \quad 0.80277$$
$$\log 0.635 \quad = \log (6.35 \times 10^{-1}) = -1.80277$$
$$\log 0.0635 = \log (6.35 \times 10^{-2}) = -2.80277$$

The table shows: (1) that the location of the decimal point determines the value of the characteristic, but does not affect the mantissa; (2) that to find the characteristic, the number must be expressed as the product of two other numbers, one of which is an integer power of 10, and the other a number containing but one digit to the left of the decimal point (Sec. 3.8); then the power of 10 is the value of the characteristic.

From the above we see that the characteristic of the logarithm may be determined by inspection. The mantissa values must be obtained from tables, called *logarithm tables* (Appendix IV).

Example 1. Multiply 235 by 86.

Solution. First find the characteristic of each number.

$$235 = 2.35 \times 10^2. \quad \text{Characteristic} = 2.$$
$$86 = 8.6 \times 10^1. \quad \text{Characteristic} = 1.$$

Next find the mantissa value for each. These values will be found in the table in Appendix IV. Add the logarithms. Then:

$$\log 235 = 2.37107$$
$$\log 86 = \underline{1.93450}$$
$$\text{add} \quad 4.30557$$

Now find the number in the logarithm table in Appendix IV corresponding to the mantissa value 30557. The number is 2021. That is:

$$\text{antilogarithm } 4.30557 = 2.021 \times 10^4 = 20,210.$$

Example 2. Divide 4.86 by 0.096.

Solution. The logarithm of 0.096 must be subtracted from the logarithm of 4.86. Therefore:

$$\log 4.86 \ = \log (4.86 \times 10^0) \ = \ \ \ 0.68664$$
$$\log 0.096 = \log (9.6 \ \ \times 10^{-2}) = -2.98227$$

When the characteristic is negative it is advisable to add and subtract 10 to and from the characteristic. Remember, the mantissa is always positive. Then:

$$\log 4.86 \ = 10.68664 - 10$$
$$\log 0.096 = \ \ \underline{8.98227 - 10}$$
$$\text{subtract} \ \ \ 1.70437$$

antilogarithm $1.70437 = 5.063 \times 10^1 = 50.63$.

Example 3. Simplify the expression $\dfrac{273 \times 0.00783}{486}$.

Solution. Subtract the logarithm of 486 from the sum of the logarithms of 273 and 0.00783. Then:

$$\log 273 \ \ \ \ \ = \ \ 2.43616$$
$$\log 0.00783 = \ \ \underline{7.89376 - 10}$$
$$\text{add} \ \ \ \ 10.32992 - 10$$

$$\log 486 \ \ \ \ \ = \ \ \underline{2.68664}$$
$$\text{subtract} \ \ \ \ 7.64328 - 10 = -3.64328$$

antilogarithm $-3.64328 = 4.398 \times 10^{-3} = 0.004398$.

Example 4. Evaluate 27.5^3.

Solution. Since $27.5^3 = 27.5 \times 27.5 \times 27.5$,
then: $\qquad \log 27.5^3 = 3 \times \log 27.5 = 3(1.43933) = 4.31799$.
$\qquad$ antilogarithm $4.31799 = 2.080 \times 10^4 = 20,800$.

The mantissa table in Appendix IV gives values for numbers containing four places only. By means of interpolation it is possible to calculate the mantissa of a number containing five places. For example, find the mantissa of 32644 from the table in Appendix IV. The mantissa of 32640 = 51375, and of 32650 = 51388. Evidently the mantissa of 32644 lies between the above values. Considering that there are ten proportional parts between 32640 and 32650, then 32644 is four proportional parts greater than 32640. The difference between the above mantissa values is 51388 − 51375 = 13. In the column marked proportional parts, for a difference of 13 in the mantissa values, four proportional parts require a correction of 5 to be added to the lower value 51375. That is:

$$\log 32644 = 4.51375 + 0.00005 = 4.51380.$$

Similarly, it is possible to determine the antilogarithm of a number to five places.

Problems

1. Perform the indicated operations: 782×74; $7340 \div 29$; 0.0756×0.34; $0.314 \div 2.14$.   *Ans.* 57,869; 253.10; 0.025704; 0.14673.

2. Simplify the expression $326 \times \frac{273}{296} \times \frac{733}{760}$.   *Ans.* 286.03.

3. Evaluate 32614×78546.   *Ans.* 2.5617×10^9.

IV. Five-Place Logarithm Table

The table on the following pages contains the mantissas of logarithms to five decimal places.   The use of the table is explained in Appendix III.   The mantissa values were calculated using 10 as a base.   This gives the *common system* of logarithms, usually denoted by the symbol log.

0—50

N	L 0	1	2	3	4	5	6	7	8	9
0	— ∞	00 000	30 103	47 712	60 206	69 897	77 815	84 510	90 309	95 424
1	00 000	04 139	07 918	11 394	14 613	17 609	20 412	23 045	25 527	27 875
2	30 103	32 222	34 242	36 173	38 021	39 794	41 497	43 136	44 716	46 240
3	47 712	49 136	50 515	51 851	53 148	54 407	55 630	56 820	57 978	59 106
4	60 206	61 278	62 325	63 347	64 345	65 321	66 276	67 210	68 124	69 020
5	69 897	70 757	71 600	72 428	73 239	74 036	74 819	75 587	76 343	77 085
6	77 815	78 533	79 239	79 934	80 618	81 291	81 954	82 607	83 251	83 885
7	84 510	85 126	85 733	86 332	86 923	87 506	88 081	88 649	89 209	89 763
8	90 309	90 849	91 381	91 908	92 428	92 942	93 450	93 952	94 448	94 939
9	95 424	95 904	96 379	96 848	97 313	97 772	98 227	98 677	99 123	99 564
10	00 000	00 432	00 860	01 284	01 703	02 119	02 531	02 938	03 342	03 743
11	04 139	04 532	04 922	05 308	05 690	06 070	06 446	06 819	07 188	07 555
12	07 918	08 279	08 636	08 991	09 342	09 691	10 037	10 380	10 721	11 059
13	11 394	11 727	12 057	12 385	12 710	13 033	13 354	13 672	13 988	14 301
14	14 613	14 922	15 229	15 534	15 836	16 137	16 435	16 732	17 026	17 319
15	17 609	17 898	18 184	18 469	18 752	19 033	19 312	19 590	19 866	20 140
16	20 412	20 683	20 952	21 219	21 484	21 748	22 011	22 272	22 531	22 789
17	23 045	23 300	23 553	23 805	24 055	24 304	24 551	24 797	25 042	25 285
18	25 527	25 768	26 007	26 245	26 482	26 717	26 951	27 184	27 416	27 646
19	27 875	28 103	28 330	28 556	28 780	29 003	29 226	29 447	29 667	29 885
20	30 103	30 320	30 535	30 750	30 963	31 175	31 387	31 597	31 806	32 015
21	32 222	32 428	32 634	32 838	33 041	33 244	33 445	33 646	33 846	34 044
22	34 242	34 439	34 635	34 830	35 025	35 218	35 411	35 603	35 793	35 984
23	36 173	36 361	36 549	36 736	36 922	37 107	37 291	37 475	37 658	37 840
24	38 021	38 202	38 382	38 561	38 739	38 917	39 094	39 270	39 445	39 620
25	39 794	39 967	40 140	40 312	40 483	40 654	40 824	40 993	41 162	41 330
26	41 497	41 664	41 830	41 996	42 160	42 325	42 488	42 651	42 813	42 975
27	43 136	43 297	43 457	43 616	43 775	43 933	44 091	44 248	44 404	44 560
28	44 716	44 871	45 025	45 179	45 332	45 484	45 637	45 788	45 939	46 090
29	46 240	46 389	46 538	46 687	46 835	46 982	47 129	47 276	47 422	47 567
30	47 712	47 857	48 001	48 144	48 287	48 430	48 572	48 714	48 855	48 996
31	49 136	49 276	49 415	49 554	49 693	49 831	49 969	50 106	50 243	50 379
32	50 515	50 651	50 786	50 920	51 055	51 188	51 322	51 455	51 587	51 720
33	51 851	51 983	52 114	52 244	52 375	52 504	52 634	52 763	52 892	53 020
34	53 148	53 275	53 403	53 529	53 656	53 782	53 908	54 033	54 158	54 283
35	54 407	54 531	54 654	54 777	54 900	55 023	55 145	55 267	55 388	55 509
36	55 630	55 751	55 871	55 991	56 110	56 229	56 348	56 467	56 585	56 703
37	56 820	56 937	57 054	57 171	57 287	57 403	57 519	57 634	57 749	57 864
38	57 978	58 092	58 206	58 320	58 433	58 546	58 659	58 771	58 883	58 995
39	59 106	59 218	59 329	59 439	59 550	59 660	59 770	59 879	59 988	60 097
40	60 206	60 314	60 423	60 531	60 638	60 746	60 853	60 959	61 066	61 172
41	61 278	61 384	61 490	61 595	61 700	61 805	61 909	62 014	62 118	62 221
42	62 325	62 428	62 531	62 634	62 737	62 839	62 941	63 043	63 144	63 246
43	63 347	63 448	63 548	63 649	63 749	63 849	63 949	64 048	64 147	64 246
44	64 345	64 444	64 542	64 640	64 738	64 836	64 933	65 031	65 128	65 225
45	65 321	65 418	65 514	65 610	65 706	65 801	65 896	65 992	66 087	66 181
46	66 276	66 370	66 464	66 558	66 652	66 745	66 839	66 932	67 025	67 117
47	67 210	67 302	67 394	67 486	67 578	67 669	67 761	67 852	67 943	68 034
48	68 124	68 215	68 305	68 395	68 485	68 574	68 664	68 753	68 842	68 931
49	69 020	69 108	69 197	69 285	69 373	69 461	69 548	69 636	69 723	69 810
50	69 897	69 984	70 070	70 157	70 243	70 329	70 415	70 501	70 586	70 672
N	L 0	1	2	3	4	5	6	7	8	9

50—100

N	L 0	1	2	3	4	5	6	7	8	9
50	69 897	69 984	70 070	70 157	70 243	70 329	70 415	70 501	70 586	70 672
51	70 757	70 842	70 927	71 012	71 096	71 181	71 265	71 349	71 433	71 517
52	71 600	71 684	71 767	71 850	71 933	72 016	72 099	72 181	72 263	72 346
53	72 428	72 509	72 591	72 673	72 754	72 835	72 916	72 997	73 078	73 159
54	73 239	73 320	73 400	73 480	73 560	73 640	73 719	73 799	73 878	73 957
55	74 036	74 115	74 194	74 273	74 351	74 429	74 507	74 586	74 663	74 741
56	74 819	74 896	74 974	75 051	75 128	75 205	75 282	75 358	75 435	75 511
57	75 587	75 664	75 740	75 815	75 891	75 967	76 042	76 118	76 193	76 268
58	76 346	76 418	76 492	76 567	76 641	76 716	76 790	76 864	76 938	77 012
59	77 085	77 159	77 232	77 305	77 379	77 452	77 525	77 597	77 670	77 743
60	77 815	77 887	77 960	78 032	78 104	78 176	78 247	78 319	78 390	78 462
61	78 533	78 604	78 675	78 746	78 817	78 888	78 958	79 029	79 099	79 169
62	79 239	79 309	79 379	79 449	79 518	79 588	79 657	79 727	79 796	79 865
63	79 934	80 003	80 072	80 140	80 209	80 277	80 346	80 414	80 482	80 550
64	80 618	80 686	80 754	80 821	80 889	80 956	81 023	81 090	81 158	81 224
65	81 291	81 358	81 425	81 491	81 558	81 624	81 690	81 757	81 823	81 889
66	81 954	82 020	82 086	82 151	82 217	82 282	82 347	82 413	82 478	82 543
67	82 607	82 672	82 737	82 802	82 866	82 930	82 995	83 059	83 123	83 187
68	83 251	83 315	83 378	83 442	83 506	83 569	83 632	83 696	83 759	83 822
69	83 885	83 948	84 011	84 073	84 136	84 198	84 261	84 323	84 386	84 448
70	84 510	84 572	84 634	84 696	84 757	84 819	84 880	84 942	85 003	85 065
71	85 126	85 187	85 248	85 309	85 370	85 431	85 491	85 552	85 612	85 673
72	85 733	85 794	85 854	85 914	85 974	86 034	86 094	86 153	86 213	86 273
73	86 332	86 392	86 451	86 510	86 570	86 629	86 688	86 747	86 806	86 864
74	86 923	86 982	87 040	87 099	87 157	87 216	87 274	87 332	87 390	87 448
75	87 506	87 564	87 622	87 679	87 737	87 795	87 852	87 910	87 967	88 024
76	88 081	88 138	88 195	88 252	88 309	88 366	88 423	88 480	88 536	88 593
77	88 649	88 705	88 762	88 818	88 874	88 930	88 986	89 042	89 098	89 154
78	89 209	89 265	89 321	89 376	89 432	89 487	89 542	89 597	89 653	89 708
79	89 763	89 818	89 873	89 927	89 982	90 037	90 091	90 146	90 200	90 255
80	90 309	90 363	90 417	90 472	90 526	90 580	90 634	90 687	90 741	90 795
81	90 849	90 902	90 956	91 009	91 062	91 116	91 169	91 222	91 275	91 328
82	91 381	91 434	91 487	91 540	91 593	91 645	91 698	91 751	91 803	91 855
83	91 908	91 960	92 012	92 065	92 117	92 169	92 221	92 273	92 324	92 376
84	92 428	92 480	92 531	92 583	92 634	92 686	92 737	92 788	92 840	92 891
85	92 942	92 993	93 044	93 095	93 146	93 197	93 247	93 298	93 349	93 399
86	93 450	93 500	93 551	93 601	93 651	93 702	93 752	93 802	93 852	93 902
87	93 952	94 002	94 052	94 101	94 151	94 201	94 250	94 300	94 349	94 399
88	94 448	94 498	94 547	94 596	94 645	94 694	94 743	94 792	94 841	94 890
89	94 939	94 988	95 036	95 085	95 134	95 182	95 231	95 279	95 328	95 376
90	95 424	95 472	95 521	95 569	95 617	95 665	95 713	95 761	95 809	95 856
91	95 904	95 952	95 999	96 047	96 095	96 142	96 190	96 237	96 284	96 332
92	96 379	96 426	96 473	96 520	96 567	96 614	96 661	96 708	96 755	96 802
93	96 848	96 895	96 942	96 988	97 035	97 081	97 128	97 174	97 220	97 267
94	97 313	97 359	97 405	97 451	97 497	97 543	97 589	97 635	97 681	97 727
95	97 772	97 818	97 864	97 909	97 955	98 000	98 046	98 091	98 137	98 182
96	98 227	98 272	98 318	98 363	98 408	98 453	98 498	98 543	98 588	98 632
97	98 677	98 722	98 767	98 811	98 856	98 900	98 945	98 989	99 034	99 078
98	99 123	99 167	99 211	99 255	99 300	99 344	99 388	99 432	99 476	99 520
99	99 564	99 607	99 651	99 695	99 739	99 782	99 826	99 870	99 913	99 957
100	00 000	00 043	00 087	00 130	00 173	00 217	00 260	00 303	00 346	00 389
N	L 0	1	2	3	4	5	6	7	8	9

100—150

N	L 0	1	2	3	4	5	6	7	8	9
100	00 000	043	087	130	173	217	260	303	346	389
101	432	475	518	561	604	647	689	732	775	817
102	860	903	945	988	*030	*072	*115	*157	*199	*242
103	01 284	326	368	410	452	494	536	578	620	662
104	703	745	787	828	870	912	953	995	*036	*078
105	02 119	160	202	243	284	325	366	407	449	490
106	531	572	612	653	694	735	776	816	857	898
107	938	979	*019	*060	*100	*141	*181	*222	*262	*302
108	03 342	383	423	463	503	543	583	623	663	703
109	743	782	822	862	902	941	981	*021	*060	*100
110	04 139	179	218	258	297	336	376	415	454	493
111	532	571	610	650	689	727	766	805	844	883
112	922	961	999	*038	*077	*115	*154	*192	*231	*269
113	05 308	346	385	423	461	500	538	576	614	652
114	690	729	767	805	843	881	918	956	994	*032
115	06 070	108	145	183	221	258	296	333	371	408
116	446	483	521	558	595	633	670	707	744	781
117	819	856	893	930	967	*004	*041	*078	*115	*151
118	07 188	225	262	298	335	372	408	445	482	518
119	555	591	628	664	700	737	773	809	846	882
120	918	954	990	*027	*063	*099	*135	*171	*207	*243
121	08 279	314	350	386	422	458	493	529	565	600
122	636	672	707	743	778	814	849	884	920	955
123	991	*026	*061	*096	*132	*167	*202	*237	*272	*307
124	09 342	377	412	447	482	517	552	587	621	656
125	691	726	760	795	830	864	899	934	968	*003
126	10 037	072	106	140	175	209	243	278	312	346
127	380	415	449	483	517	551	585	619	653	687
128	721	755	789	823	857	890	924	958	992	*025
129	11 059	093	126	160	193	227	261	294	327	361
130	394	428	461	494	528	561	594	628	661	694
131	727	760	793	826	860	893	926	959	992	*024
132	12 057	090	123	156	189	222	254	287	320	352
133	385	418	450	483	516	548	581	613	646	678
134	710	743	775	808	840	872	905	937	969	*001
135	13 033	066	098	130	162	194	226	258	290	322
136	354	386	418	450	481	513	545	577	609	640
137	672	704	735	767	799	830	862	893	925	956
138	988	*019	*051	*082	*114	*145	*176	*208	*239	*270
139	14 301	333	364	395	426	457	489	520	551	582
140	613	644	675	706	737	768	799	829	860	891
141	922	953	983	*014	*045	*076	*106	*137	*168	*198
142	15 229	259	290	320	351	381	412	442	473	503
143	534	564	594	625	655	685	715	746	776	806
144	836	866	897	927	957	987	*017	*047	*077	*107
145	16 137	167	197	227	256	286	316	346	376	406
146	435	465	495	524	554	584	613	643	673	702
147	732	761	791	820	850	879	909	938	967	997
148	17 026	056	085	114	143	173	202	231	260	289
149	319	348	377	406	435	464	493	522	551	580
150	17 609	638	667	696	725	754	782	811	840	869
N	L 0	1	2	3	4	5	6	7	8	9

P P

	44	43	42
1	4.4	4.3	4.2
2	8.8	8.6	8.4
3	13.2	12.9	12.6
4	17.6	17.2	16.8
5	22.0	21.5	21.0
6	26.4	25.8	25.2
7	30.8	30.1	29.4
8	35.2	34.4	33.6
9	39.6	38.7	37.8

	41	40	39
1	4.1	4.0	3.9
2	8.2	8.0	7.8
3	12.3	12.0	11.7
4	16.4	16.0	15.6
5	20.5	20.0	19.5
6	24.6	24.0	23.4
7	28.7	28.0	27.3
8	32.8	32.0	31.2
9	36.9	36.0	35.1

	38	37	36
1	3.8	3.7	3.6
2	7.6	7.4	7.2
3	11.4	11.1	10.8
4	15.2	14.8	14.4
5	19.0	18.5	18.0
6	22.8	22.2	21.6
7	26.6	25.9	25.2
8	30.4	29.6	28.8
9	34.2	33.3	32.4

	35	34	33
1	3.5	3.4	3.3
2	7.0	6.8	6.6
3	10.5	10.2	9.9
4	14.0	13.6	13.2
5	17.5	17.0	16.5
6	21.0	20.4	19.8
7	24.5	23.8	23.1
8	28.0	27.2	26.4
9	31.5	30.6	29.7

	32	31	30
1	3.2	3.1	3.0
2	6.4	6.2	6.0
3	9.6	9.3	9.0
4	12.8	12.4	12.0
5	16.0	15.5	15.0
6	19.2	18.6	18.0
7	22.4	21.7	21.0
8	25.6	24.8	24.0
9	28.8	27.9	27.0

P P

N	L 0	1	2	3	4	5	6	7	8	9
150	17 609	638	667	696	725	754	782	811	840	869
151	898	926	955	984	*013	*041	*070	*099	*127	*156
152	18 184	213	241	270	298	327	355	384	412	441
153	469	498	526	554	583	611	639	667	696	724
154	752	780	808	837	865	893	921	949	977	*005
155	19 033	061	089	117	145	173	201	229	257	285
156	312	340	368	396	424	451	479	507	535	562
157	590	618	645	673	700	728	756	783	811	838
158	866	893	921	948	976	*003	*030	*058	*085	*112
159	20 140	167	194	222	249	276	303	330	358	385
160	412	439	466	493	520	548	575	602	629	656
161	683	710	737	763	790	817	844	871	898	925
162	952	978	*005	*032	*059	*085	*112	*139	*165	*192
163	21 219	245	272	299	325	352	378	405	431	458
164	484	511	537	564	590	617	643	669	696	722
165	748	775	801	827	854	880	906	932	958	985
166	22 011	037	063	089	115	141	167	194	220	246
167	272	298	324	350	376	401	427	453	479	505
168	531	557	583	608	634	660	686	712	737	763
169	789	814	840	866	891	917	943	968	994	*019
170	23 045	070	096	121	147	172	198	223	249	274
171	300	325	350	376	401	426	452	477	502	528
172	553	578	603	629	654	679	704	729	754	779
173	805	830	855	880	905	930	955	980	*005	*030
174	24 055	080	105	130	155	180	204	229	254	279
175	304	329	353	378	403	428	452	477	502	527
176	551	576	601	625	650	674	699	724	748	773
177	797	822	846	871	895	920	944	969	993	*018
178	25 042	066	091	115	139	164	188	212	237	261
179	285	310	334	358	382	406	431	455	479	503
180	527	551	575	600	624	648	672	696	720	744
181	768	792	816	840	864	888	912	935	959	983
182	26 007	031	055	079	102	126	150	174	198	221
183	245	269	293	316	340	364	387	411	435	458
184	482	505	529	553	576	600	623	647	670	694
185	717	741	764	788	811	834	858	881	905	928
186	951	975	998	*021	*045	*068	*091	*114	*138	*161
187	27 184	207	231	254	277	300	323	346	370	393
188	416	439	462	485	508	531	554	577	600	623
189	646	669	692	715	738	761	784	807	830	852
190	875	898	921	944	967	989	*012	*035	*058	*081
191	28 103	126	149	171	194	217	240	262	285	307
192	330	353	375	398	421	443	466	488	511	533
193	556	578	601	623	646	668	691	713	735	758
194	780	803	825	847	870	892	914	937	959	981
195	29 003	026	048	070	092	115	137	159	181	203
196	226	248	270	292	314	336	358	380	403	425
197	447	469	491	513	535	557	579	601	623	645
198	667	688	710	732	754	776	798	820	842	863
199	885	907	929	951	973	994	*016	*038	*060	*081
200	30 103	125	146	168	190	211	233	255	276	298
N	L 0	1	2	3	4	5	6	7	8	9

P P

	29	28
1	2.9	2.8
2	5.8	5.6
3	8.7	8.4
4	11.6	11.2
5	14.5	14.0
6	17.4	16.8
7	20.3	19.6
8	23.2	22.4
9	26.1	25.2

	27	26
1	2.7	2.6
2	5.4	5.2
3	8.1	7.8
4	10.8	10.4
5	13.5	13.0
6	16.2	15.6
7	18.9	18.2
8	21.6	20.8
9	24.3	23.4

	25
1	2.5
2	5.0
3	7.5
4	10.0
5	12.5
6	15.0
7	17.5
8	20.0
9	22.5

	24	23
1	2.4	2.3
2	4.8	4.6
3	7.2	6.9
4	9.6	9.2
5	12.0	11.5
6	14.4	13.8
7	16.8	16.1
8	19.2	18.4
9	21.6	20.7

	22	21
1	2.2	2.1
2	4.4	4.2
3	6.6	6.3
4	8.8	8.4
5	11.0	10.5
6	13.2	12.6
7	15.4	14.7
8	17.6	16.8
9	19.8	18.9

P P

200—250

N	L 0	1	2	3	4	5	6	7	8	9
200	30 103	125	146	168	190	211	233	255	276	298
201	320	341	363	384	406	428	449	471	492	514
202	535	557	578	600	621	643	664	685	707	728
203	750	771	792	814	835	856	878	899	920	942
204	963	984	*006	*027	*048	*069	*091	*112	*133	*154
205	31 175	197	218	239	260	281	302	323	345	366
206	387	408	429	450	471	492	513	534	555	576
207	597	618	639	660	681	702	723	744	765	785
208	806	827	848	869	890	911	931	952	973	994
209	32 015	035	056	077	098	118	139	160	181	201
210	222	243	263	284	305	325	346	366	387	408
211	428	449	469	490	510	531	552	572	593	613
212	634	654	675	695	715	736	756	777	797	818
213	838	858	879	899	919	940	960	980	*001	*021
214	33 041	062	082	102	122	143	163	183	203	224
215	244	264	284	304	325	345	365	385	405	425
216	445	465	486	506	526	546	566	586	606	626
217	646	666	686	706	726	746	766	786	806	826
218	846	866	885	905	925	945	965	985	*005	*025
219	34 044	064	084	104	124	143	163	183	203	223
220	242	262	282	301	321	341	361	380	400	420
221	439	459	479	498	518	537	557	577	596	616
222	635	655	674	694	713	733	753	772	792	811
223	830	850	869	889	908	928	947	967	986	*005
224	35 025	044	064	083	102	122	141	160	180	199
225	218	238	257	276	295	315	334	353	372	392
226	411	430	449	468	488	507	526	545	564	583
227	603	622	641	660	679	698	717	736	755	774
228	793	813	832	851	870	889	908	927	946	965
229	984	*003	*021	*040	*059	*078	*097	*116	*135	*154
230	36 173	192	211	229	248	267	286	305	324	342
231	361	380	399	418	436	455	474	493	511	530
232	549	568	586	605	624	642	661	680	698	717
233	736	754	773	791	810	829	847	866	884	903
234	922	940	959	977	996	*014	*033	*051	*070	*088
235	37 107	125	144	162	181	199	218	236	254	273
236	291	310	328	346	365	383	401	420	438	457
237	475	493	511	530	548	566	585	603	621	639
238	658	676	694	712	731	749	767	785	803	822
239	840	858	876	894	912	931	949	967	985	*003
240	38 021	039	057	075	093	112	130	148	166	184
241	202	220	238	256	274	292	310	328	346	364
242	382	399	417	435	453	471	489	507	525	543
243	561	578	596	614	632	650	668	686	703	721
244	739	757	775	792	810	828	846	863	881	899
245	917	934	952	970	987	*005	*023	*041	*058	*076
246	39 094	111	129	146	164	182	199	217	235	252
247	270	287	305	322	340	358	375	393	410	428
248	445	463	480	498	515	533	550	568	585	602
249	620	637	655	672	690	707	724	742	759	777
250	794	811	829	846	863	881	898	915	933	950
N	L 0	1	2	3	4	5	6	7	8	9

P P

	22	21
1	2.2	2.1
2	4.4	4.2
3	6.6	6.3
4	8.8	8.4
5	11.0	10.5
6	13.2	12.6
7	15.4	14.7
8	17.6	16.8
9	19.8	18.9

	20
1	2.0
2	4.0
3	6.0
4	8.0
5	10.0
6	12.0
7	14.0
8	16.0
9	18.0

	19
1	1.9
2	3.8
3	5.7
4	7.6
5	9.5
6	11.4
7	13.3
8	15.2
9	17.1

	18
1	1.8
2	3.6
3	5.4
4	7.2
5	9.0
6	10.8
7	12.6
8	14.4
9	16.2

	17
1	1.7
2	3.4
3	5.1
4	6.8
5	8.5
6	10.2
7	11.9
8	13.6
9	15.3

250—300

N	L 0	1	2	3	4	5	6	7	8	9
250	39 794	811	829	846	863	881	898	915	933	950
251	967	985	*002	*019	*037	*054	*071	*088	*106	*123
252	40 140	157	175	192	209	226	243	261	278	295
253	312	329	346	364	381	398	415	432	449	466
254	483	500	518	535	552	569	586	603	620	637
255	654	671	688	705	722	739	756	773	790	807
256	824	841	858	875	892	909	926	943	960	976
257	993	*010	*027	*044	*061	*078	*095	*111	*128	*145
258	41 162	179	196	212	229	246	263	280	296	313
259	330	347	363	380	397	414	430	447	464	481
260	497	514	531	547	564	581	597	614	631	647
261	664	681	697	714	731	747	764	780	797	814
262	830	847	863	880	896	913	929	946	963	979
263	996	*012	*029	*045	*062	*078	*095	*111	*127	*144
264	42 160	177	193	210	226	243	259	275	292	308
265	325	341	357	374	390	406	423	439	455	472
266	488	504	521	537	553	570	586	602	619	635
267	651	667	684	700	716	732	749	765	781	797
268	813	830	846	862	878	894	911	927	943	959
269	975	991	*008	*024	*040	*056	*072	*088	*104	*120
270	43 136	152	169	185	201	217	233	249	265	281
271	297	313	329	345	361	377	393	409	425	441
272	457	473	489	505	521	537	553	569	584	600
273	616	632	648	664	680	696	712	727	743	759
274	775	791	807	823	838	854	870	886	902	917
275	933	949	965	981	996	*012	*028	*044	*059	*075
276	44 091	107	122	138	154	170	185	201	217	232
277	248	264	279	295	311	326	342	358	373	389
278	404	420	436	451	467	483	498	514	529	545
279	560	576	592	607	623	638	654	669	685	700
280	716	731	747	762	778	793	809	824	840	855
281	871	886	902	917	932	948	963	979	994	*010
282	45 025	040	056	071	086	102	117	133	148	163
283	179	194	209	225	240	255	271	286	301	317
284	332	347	362	378	393	408	423	439	454	469
285	484	500	515	530	545	561	576	591	606	621
286	637	652	667	682	697	712	728	743	758	773
287	788	803	818	834	849	864	879	894	909	924
288	939	954	969	984	*000	*015	*030	*045	*060	*075
289	46 090	105	120	135	150	165	180	195	210	225
290	240	255	270	285	300	315	330	345	359	374
291	389	404	419	434	449	464	479	494	509	523
292	538	553	568	583	598	613	627	642	657	672
293	687	702	716	731	746	761	776	790	805	820
294	835	850	864	879	894	909	923	938	953	967
295	982	997	*012	*026	*041	*056	*070	*085	*100	*114
296	47 129	144	159	173	188	202	217	232	246	261
297	276	290	305	319	334	349	363	378	392	407
298	422	436	451	465	480	494	509	524	538	553
299	567	582	596	611	625	640	654	669	683	698
300	712	727	741	756	770	784	799	813	828	842
N	L 0	1	2	3	4	5	6	7	8	9

P P

18
1 | 1.8
2 | 3.6
3 | 5.4
4 | 7.2
5 | 9.0
6 | 10.8
7 | 12.6
8 | 14.4
9 | 16.2

17
1 | 1.7
2 | 3.4
3 | 5.1
4 | 6.8
5 | 8.5
6 | 10.2
7 | 11.9
8 | 13.6
9 | 15.3

16
1 | 1.6
2 | 3.2
3 | 4.8
4 | 6.4
5 | 8.0
6 | 9.6
7 | 11.2
8 | 12.8
9 | 14.4

15
1 | 1.5
2 | 3.0
3 | 4.5
4 | 6.0
5 | 7.5
6 | 9.0
7 | 10.5
8 | 12.0
9 | 13.5

14
1 | 1.4
2 | 2.8
3 | 4.2
4 | 5.6
5 | 7.0
6 | 8.4
7 | 9.8
8 | 11.2
9 | 12.6

300—350

N	L 0	1	2	3	4	5	6	7	8	9
300	47 712	727	741	756	770	784	799	813	828	842
301	857	871	885	900	914	929	943	958	972	986
302	48 001	015	029	044	058	073	087	101	116	130
303	144	159	173	187	202	216	230	244	259	273
304	287	302	316	330	344	359	373	387	401	416
305	430	444	458	473	487	501	515	530	544	558
306	572	586	601	615	629	643	657	671	686	700
307	714	728	742	756	770	785	799	813	827	841
308	855	869	883	897	911	926	940	954	968	982
309	996	*010	*024	*038	*052	*066	*080	*094	*108	*122
310	49 136	150	164	178	192	206	220	234	248	262
311	276	290	304	318	332	346	360	374	388	402
312	415	429	443	457	471	485	499	513	527	541
313	554	568	582	596	610	624	638	651	665	679
314	693	707	721	734	748	762	776	790	803	817
315	831	845	859	872	886	900	914	927	941	955
316	969	982	996	*010	*024	*037	*051	*065	*079	*092
317	50 106	120	133	147	161	174	188	202	215	229
318	243	256	270	284	297	311	325	338	352	365
319	379	393	406	420	433	447	461	474	488	501
320	515	529	542	556	569	583	596	610	623	637
321	651	664	678	691	705	718	732	745	759	772
322	786	799	813	826	840	853	866	880	893	907
323	920	934	947	961	974	987	*001	*014	*028	*041
324	51 055	068	081	095	108	121	135	148	162	175
325	188	202	215	228	242	255	268	282	295	308
326	322	335	348	362	375	388	402	415	428	441
327	455	468	481	495	508	521	534	548	561	574
328	587	601	614	627	640	654	667	680	693	706
329	720	733	746	759	772	786	799	812	825	838
330	851	865	878	891	904	917	930	943	957	970
331	983	996	*009	*022	*035	*048	*061	*075	*088	*101
332	52 114	127	140	153	166	179	192	205	218	231
333	244	257	270	284	297	310	323	336	349	362
334	375	388	401	414	427	440	453	466	479	492
335	504	517	530	543	556	569	582	595	608	621
336	634	647	660	673	686	699	711	724	737	750
337	763	776	789	802	815	827	840	853	866	879
338	892	905	917	930	943	956	969	982	994	*007
339	53 020	033	046	058	071	084	097	110	122	135
340	148	161	173	186	199	212	224	237	250	263
341	275	288	301	314	326	339	352	364	377	390
342	403	415	428	441	453	466	479	491	504	517
343	529	542	555	567	580	593	605	618	631	643
344	656	668	681	694	706	719	732	744	757	769
345	782	794	807	820	832	845	857	870	882	895
346	908	920	933	945	958	970	983	995	*008	*020
347	54 033	045	058	070	083	095	108	120	133	145
348	158	170	183	195	208	220	233	245	258	270
349	283	295	307	320	332	345	357	370	382	394
	407	419	432	444	456	469	481	494	506	518
	1	2	3	4	5	6	7	8	9	

P P

15
1	1.5
2	3.0
3	4.5
4	6.0
5	7.5
6	9.0
7	10.5
8	12.0
9	13.5

14
1	1.4
2	2.8
3	4.2
4	5.6
5	7.0
6	8.4
7	9.8
8	11.2
9	12.6

13
1	1.3
2	2.6
3	3.9
4	5.2
5	6.5
6	7.8
7	9.1
8	10.4
9	11.7

12
1	1.2
2	2.4
3	3.6
4	4.8
5	6.0
6	7.2
7	8.4
8	9.6
9	10.8

350—400

N	L 0	1	2	3	4	5	6	7	8	9
350	54 407	419	432	444	456	469	481	494	506	518
351	531	543	555	568	580	593	605	617	630	642
352	654	667	679	691	704	716	728	741	753	765
353	777	790	802	814	827	839	851	864	876	888
354	900	913	925	937	949	962	974	986	998	*011
355	55 023	035	047	060	072	084	096	108	121	133
356	145	157	169	182	194	206	218	230	242	255
357	267	279	291	303	315	328	340	352	364	376
358	388	400	413	425	437	449	461	473	485	497
359	509	522	534	546	558	570	582	594	606	618
360	630	642	654	666	678	691	703	715	727	739
361	751	763	775	787	799	811	823	835	847	859
362	871	883	895	907	919	931	943	955	967	979
363	991	*003	*015	*027	*038	*050	*062	*074	*086	*098
364	56 110	122	134	146	158	170	182	194	205	217
365	229	241	253	265	277	289	301	312	324	336
366	348	360	372	384	396	407	419	431	443	455
367	467	478	490	502	514	526	538	549	561	573
368	585	597	608	620	632	644	656	667	679	691
369	703	714	726	738	750	761	773	785	797	808
370	820	832	844	855	867	879	891	902	914	926
371	937	949	961	972	984	996	*008	*019	*031	*043
372	57 054	066	078	089	101	113	124	136	148	159
373	171	183	194	206	217	229	241	252	264	276
374	287	299	310	322	334	345	357	368	380	392
375	403	415	426	438	449	461	473	484	496	507
376	519	530	542	553	565	576	588	600	611	623
377	634	646	657	669	680	692	703	715	726	738
378	749	761	772	784	795	807	818	830	841	852
379	864	875	887	898	910	921	933	944	955	967
380	978	990	*001	*013	*024	*035	*047	*058	*070	*081
381	58 092	104	115	127	138	149	161	172	184	195
382	206	218	229	240	252	263	274	286	297	309
383	320	331	343	354	365	377	388	399	410	422
384	433	444	456	467	478	490	501	512	524	535
385	546	557	569	580	591	602	614	625	636	647
386	659	670	681	692	704	715	726	737	749	760
387	771	782	794	805	816	827	838	850	861	872
388	883	894	906	917	928	939	950	961	973	984
389	995	*006	*017	*028	*040	*051	*062	*073	*084	*095
390	59 106	118	129	140	151	162	173	184	195	207
391	218	229	240	251	262	273	284	295	306	318
392	329	340	351	362	373	384	395	406	417	428
393	439	450	461	472	483	494	506	517	528	539
394	550	561	572	583	594	605	616	627	638	649
395	660	671	682	693	704	715	726	737	748	759
396	770	780	791	802	813	824	835	846	857	868
397	879	890	901	912	923	934	945	956	966	977
398	988	999	*010	*021	*032	*043	*054	*065	*076	*086
399	60 097	108	119	130	141	152	163	173	184	195
400	206	217	228	239	249	260	271	282	293	304
N	L 0	1	2	3	4	5	6	7	8	9

P P

13

1	1.3
2	2.6
3	3.9
4	5.2
5	6.5
6	7.8
7	9.1
8	10.4
9	11.7

12

1	1.2
2	2.4
3	3.6
4	4.8
5	6.0
6	7.2
7	8.4
8	9.6
9	10.8

11

1	1.1
2	2.2
3	3.3
4	4.4
5	5.5
6	6.6
7	7.7
8	8.8
9	9.9

10

1	1.0
2	2.0
3	3.0
4	4.0
5	5.0
6	6.0
7	7.0
8	8.0
9	9.0

400—450

N	L0	1	2	3	4	5	6	7	8	9
400	60 206	217	228	239	249	260	271	282	293	304
401	314	325	336	347	358	369	379	390	401	412
402	423	433	444	455	466	477	487	498	509	520
403	531	541	552	563	574	584	595	606	617	627
404	638	649	660	670	681	692	703	713	724	735
405	746	756	767	778	788	799	810	821	831	842
406	853	863	874	885	895	906	917	927	938	949
407	959	970	981	991	*002	*013	*023	*034	*045	*055
408	61 066	077	087	098	109	119	130	140	151	162
409	172	183	194	204	215	225	236	247	257	268
410	278	289	300	310	321	331	342	352	363	374
411	384	395	405	416	426	437	448	458	469	479
412	490	500	511	521	532	542	553	563	574	584
413	595	606	616	627	637	648	658	669	679	690
414	700	711	721	731	742	752	763	773	784	794
415	805	815	826	836	847	857	868	878	888	899
416	909	920	930	941	951	962	972	982	993	*003
417	62 014	024	034	045	055	066	076	086	097	107
418	118	128	138	149	159	170	180	190	201	211
419	221	232	242	252	263	273	284	294	304	315
420	325	335	346	356	366	377	387	397	408	418
421	428	439	449	459	469	480	490	500	511	521
422	531	542	552	562	572	583	593	603	613	624
423	634	644	655	665	675	685	696	706	716	726
424	737	747	757	767	778	788	798	808	818	829
425	839	849	859	870	880	890	900	910	921	931
426	941	951	961	972	982	992	*002	*012	*022	*033
427	63 043	053	063	073	083	094	104	114	124	134
428	144	155	165	175	185	195	205	215	225	236
429	246	256	266	276	286	296	306	317	327	337
430	347	357	367	377	387	397	407	417	428	438
431	448	458	468	478	488	498	508	518	528	538
432	548	558	568	579	589	599	609	619	629	639
433	649	659	669	679	689	699	709	719	729	739
434	749	759	769	779	789	799	809	819	829	839
435	849	859	869	879	889	899	909	919	929	939
436	949	959	969	979	988	998	*008	*018	*028	*038
437	64 048	058	068	078	088	098	108	118	128	137
438	147	157	167	177	187	197	207	217	227	237
439	246	256	266	276	286	296	306	316	326	335
440	345	355	365	375	385	395	404	414	424	434
441	444	454	464	473	483	493	503	513	523	532
442	542	552	562	572	582	591	601	611	621	631
443	640	650	660	670	680	689	699	709	719	729
444	738	748	758	768	777	787	797	807	816	826
445	836	846	856	865	875	885	895	904	914	924
446	933	943	953	963	972	982	992	*002	*011	*021
447	65 031	040	050	060	070	079	089	099	108	118
448	128	137	147	157	167	176	186	196	205	215
449	225	234	244	254	263	273	283	292	302	312
	321	331	341	350	360	369	379	389	398	408
	1	2	3	4	5	6	7	8	9	

P P

11

1	1.1
2	2.2
3	3.3
4	4.4
5	5.5
6	6.6
7	7.7
8	8.8
9	9.9

10

1	1.0
2	2.0
3	3.0
4	4.0
5	5.0
6	6.0
7	7.0
8	8.0
9	9.0

9

1	0.9
2	1.8
3	2.7
4	3.6
5	4.5
6	5.4
7	6.3
8	7.2
9	8.1

450—500

N	L 0	1	2	3	4	5	6	7	8	9
450	65 321	331	341	350	360	369	379	389	398	408
451	418	427	437	447	456	466	475	485	495	504
452	514	523	533	543	552	562	571	581	591	600
453	610	619	629	639	648	658	667	677	686	696
454	706	715	725	734	744	753	763	772	782	792
455	801	811	820	830	839	849	858	868	877	887
456	896	906	916	925	935	944	954	963	973	982
457	992	*001	*011	*020	*030	*039	*049	*058	*068	*077
458	66 087	096	106	115	124	134	143	153	162	172
459	181	191	200	210	219	229	238	247	257	266
460	276	285	295	304	314	323	332	342	351	361
461	370	380	389	398	408	417	427	436	445	455
462	464	474	483	492	502	511	521	530	539	549
463	558	567	577	586	596	605	614	624	633	642
464	652	661	671	680	689	699	708	717	727	736
465	745	755	764	773	783	792	801	811	820	829
466	839	848	857	867	876	885	894	904	913	922
467	932	941	950	960	969	978	987	997	*006	*015
468	67 025	034	043	052	062	071	080	089	099	108
469	117	127	136	145	154	164	173	182	191	201
470	210	219	228	237	247	256	265	274	284	293
471	302	311	321	330	339	348	357	367	376	385
472	394	403	413	422	431	440	449	459	468	477
473	486	495	504	514	523	532	541	550	560	569
474	578	587	596	605	614	624	633	642	651	660
475	669	679	688	697	706	715	724	733	742	752
476	761	770	779	788	797	806	815	825	834	843
477	852	861	870	879	888	897	906	916	925	934
478	943	952	961	970	979	988	997	*006	*015	*024
479	68 034	043	052	061	070	079	088	097	106	115
480	124	133	142	151	160	169	178	187	196	205
481	215	224	233	242	251	260	269	278	287	296
482	305	314	323	332	341	350	359	368	377	386
483	395	404	413	422	431	440	449	458	467	476
484	485	494	502	511	520	529	538	547	556	565
485	574	583	592	601	610	619	628	637	646	655
486	664	673	681	690	699	708	717	726	735	744
487	753	762	771	780	789	797	806	815	824	833
488	842	851	860	869	878	886	895	904	913	922
489	931	940	949	958	966	975	984	993	*002	*011
490	69 020	028	037	046	055	064	073	082	090	099
491	108	117	126	135	144	152	161	170	179	188
492	197	205	214	223	232	241	249	258	267	276
493	285	294	302	311	320	329	338	346	355	364
494	373	381	390	399	408	417	425	434	443	452
495	461	469	478	487	496	504	513	522	531	539
496	548	557	566	574	583	592	601	609	618	627
497	636	644	653	662	671	679	688	697	705	714
498	723	732	740	749	758	767	775	784	793	801
499	810	819	827	836	845	854	862	871	880	888
500	897	906	914	923	932	940	949	958	966	975
N	L 0	1	2	3	4	5	6	7	8	9

P P

10

1	1.0
2	2.0
3	3.0
4	4.0
5	5.0
6	6.0
7	7.0
8	8.0
9	9.0

9

1	0.9
2	1.8
3	2.7
4	3.6
5	4.5
6	5.4
7	6.3
8	7.2
9	8.1

8

1	0.8
2	1.6
3	2.4
4	3.2
5	4.0
6	4.8
7	5.6
8	6.4
9	7.2

500—550

N	L 0	1	2	3	4	5	6	7	8	9
500	69 897	906	914	923	932	940	949	958	966	975
501	984	992	*001	*010	*018	*027	*036	*044	*053	*062
502	70 070	079	088	096	105	114	122	131	140	148
503	157	165	174	183	191	200	209	217	226	234
504	243	252	260	269	278	286	295	303	312	321
505	329	338	346	355	364	372	381	389	398	406
506	415	424	432	441	449	458	467	475	484	492
507	501	509	518	526	535	544	552	561	569	578
508	586	595	603	612	621	629	638	646	655	663
509	672	680	689	697	706	714	723	731	740	749
510	757	766	774	783	791	800	808	817	825	834
511	842	851	859	868	876	885	893	902	910	919
512	927	935	944	952	961	969	978	986	995	*003
513	71 012	020	029	037	046	054	063	071	079	088
514	096	105	113	122	130	139	147	155	164	172
515	181	189	198	206	214	223	231	240	248	257
516	265	273	282	290	299	307	315	324	332	341
517	349	357	366	374	383	391	399	408	416	425
518	433	441	450	458	466	475	483	492	500	508
519	517	525	533	542	550	559	567	575	584	592
520	600	609	617	625	634	642	650	659	667	675
521	684	692	700	709	717	725	734	742	750	759
522	767	775	784	792	800	809	817	825	834	842
523	850	858	867	875	883	892	900	908	917	925
524	933	941	950	958	966	975	983	991	999	*008
525	72 016	024	032	041	049	057	066	074	082	090
526	099	107	115	123	132	140	148	156	165	173
527	181	189	198	206	214	222	230	239	247	255
528	263	272	280	288	296	304	313	321	329	337
529	346	354	362	370	378	387	395	403	411	419
530	428	436	444	452	460	469	477	485	493	501
531	509	518	526	534	542	550	558	567	575	583
532	591	599	607	616	624	632	640	648	656	665
533	673	681	689	697	705	713	722	730	738	746
534	754	762	770	779	787	795	803	811	819	827
535	835	843	852	860	868	876	884	892	900	908
536	916	925	933	941	949	957	965	973	981	989
537	997	*006	*014	*022	*030	*038	*046	*054	*062	*070
538	73 078	086	094	102	111	119	127	135	143	151
539	159	167	175	183	191	199	207	215	223	231
540	239	247	255	263	272	280	288	296	304	312
541	320	328	336	344	352	360	368	376	384	392
542	400	408	416	424	432	440	448	456	464	472
543	480	488	496	504	512	520	528	536	544	552
544	560	568	576	584	592	600	608	616	624	632
545	640	648	656	664	672	679	687	695	703	711
546	719	727	735	743	751	759	767	775	783	791
547	799	807	815	823	830	838	846	854	862	870
548	878	886	894	902	910	918	926	933	941	949
549	957	965	973	981	989	997	*005	*013	*020	*028
550	74 036	044	052	060	068	076	084	092	099	107
N	L 0	1	2	3	4	5	6	7	8	9

P P

9
1	0.9
2	1.8
3	2.7
4	3.6
5	4.5
6	5.4
7	6.3
8	7.2
9	8.1

8
1	0.8
2	1.6
3	2.4
4	3.2
5	4.0
6	4.8
7	5.6
8	6.4
9	7.2

7
1	0.7
2	1.4
3	2.1
4	2.8
5	3.5
6	4.2
7	4.9
8	5.6
9	6.3

N	L 0	1	2	3	4	5	6	7	8	9
550	74 036	044	052	060	068	076	084	092	099	107
551	115	123	131	139	147	155	162	170	178	186
552	194	202	210	218	225	233	241	249	257	265
553	273	280	288	296	304	312	320	327	335	343
554	351	359	367	374	382	390	398	406	414	421
555	429	437	445	453	461	468	476	484	492	500
556	507	515	523	531	539	547	554	562	570	578
557	586	593	601	609	617	624	632	640	648	656
558	663	671	679	687	695	702	710	718	726	733
559	741	749	757	764	772	780	788	796	803	811
560	819	827	834	842	850	858	865	873	881	889
561	896	904	912	920	927	935	943	950	958	966
562	974	981	989	997	*005	*012	*020	*028	*035	*043
563	75 051	059	066	074	082	089	097	105	113	120
564	128	136	143	151	159	166	174	182	189	197
565	205	213	220	228	236	243	251	259	266	274
566	282	289	297	305	312	320	328	335	343	351
567	358	366	374	381	389	397	404	412	420	427
568	435	442	450	458	465	473	481	488	496	504
569	511	519	526	534	542	549	557	565	572	580
570	587	595	603	610	618	626	633	641	648	656
571	664	671	679	686	694	702	709	717	724	732
572	740	747	755	762	770	778	785	793	800	808
573	815	823	831	838	846	853	861	868	876	884
574	891	899	906	914	921	929	937	944	952	959
575	967	974	982	989	997	*005	*012	*020	*027	*035
576	76 042	050	057	065	072	080	087	095	103	110
577	118	125	133	140	148	155	163	170	178	185
578	193	200	208	215	223	230	238	245	253	260
579	268	275	283	290	298	305	313	320	328	335
580	343	350	358	365	373	380	388	395	403	410
581	418	425	433	440	448	455	462	470	477	485
582	492	500	507	515	522	530	537	545	552	559
583	567	574	582	589	597	604	612	619	626	634
584	641	649	656	664	671	678	686	693	701	708
585	716	723	730	738	745	753	760	768	775	782
586	790	797	805	812	819	827	834	842	849	856
587	864	871	879	886	893	901	908	916	923	930
588	938	945	953	960	967	975	982	989	997	*004
589	77 012	019	026	034	041	048	056	063	070	078
590	085	093	100	107	115	122	129	137	144	151
591	159	166	173	181	188	195	203	210	217	225
592	232	240	247	254	262	269	276	283	291	298
593	305	313	320	327	335	342	349	357	364	371
594	379	386	393	401	408	415	422	430	437	444
595	452	459	466	474	481	488	495	503	510	517
596	525	532	539	546	554	561	568	576	583	590
597	597	605	612	619	627	634	641	648	656	663
598	670	677	685	692	699	706	714	721	728	735
599	743	750	757	764	772	779	786	793	801	808
600	815	822	830	837	844	851	859	866	873	880
N	L 0	1	2	3	4	5	6	7	8	9

P P

8	
1	0.8
2	1.6
3	2.4
4	3.2
5	4.0
6	4.8
7	5.6
8	6.4
9	7.2

7	
1	0.7
2	1.4
3	2.1
4	2.8
5	3.5
6	4.2
7	4.9
8	5.6
9	6.3

N	L 0	1	2	3	4	5	6	7	8	9
600	77 815	822	830	837	844	851	859	866	873	880
601	887	895	902	909	916	924	931	938	945	952
602	960	967	974	981	988	996	*003	*010	*017	*025
603	78 032	039	046	053	061	068	075	082	089	097
604	104	111	118	125	132	140	147	154	161	168
605	176	183	190	197	204	211	219	226	233	240
606	247	254	262	269	276	283	290	297	305	312
607	319	326	333	340	347	355	362	369	376	383
608	390	398	405	412	419	426	433	440	447	455
609	462	469	476	483	490	497	504	512	519	526
610	533	540	547	554	561	569	576	583	590	597
611	604	611	618	625	633	640	647	654	661	668
612	675	682	689	696	704	711	718	725	732	739
613	746	753	760	767	774	781	789	796	803	810
614	817	824	831	838	845	852	859	866	873	880
615	888	895	902	909	916	923	930	937	944	951
616	958	965	972	979	986	993	*000	*007	*014	*021
617	79 029	036	043	050	057	064	071	078	085	092
618	099	106	113	120	127	134	141	148	155	162
619	169	176	183	190	197	204	211	218	225	232
620	239	246	253	260	267	274	281	288	295	302
621	309	316	323	330	337	344	351	358	365	372
622	379	386	393	400	407	414	421	428	435	442
623	449	456	463	470	477	484	491	498	505	511
624	518	525	532	539	546	553	560	567	574	581
625	588	595	602	609	616	623	630	637	644	650
626	657	664	671	678	685	692	699	706	713	720
627	727	734	741	748	754	761	768	775	782	789
628	796	803	810	817	824	831	837	844	851	858
629	865	872	879	886	893	900	906	913	920	927
630	934	941	948	955	962	969	975	982	989	996
631	80 003	010	017	024	030	037	044	051	058	065
632	072	079	085	092	099	106	113	120	127	134
633	140	147	154	161	168	175	182	188	195	202
634	209	216	223	229	236	243	250	257	264	271
635	277	284	291	298	305	312	318	325	332	339
636	346	353	359	366	373	380	387	393	400	407
637	414	421	428	434	441	448	455	462	468	475
638	482	489	496	502	509	516	523	530	536	543
639	550	557	564	570	577	584	591	598	604	611
640	618	625	632	638	645	652	659	665	672	679
641	686	693	699	706	713	720	726	733	740	747
642	754	760	767	774	781	787	794	801	808	814
643	821	828	835	841	848	855	862	868	875	882
644	889	895	902	909	916	922	929	936	943	949
645	956	963	969	976	983	990	996	*003	*010	*017
646	81 023	030	037	043	050	057	064	070	077	084
647	090	097	104	111	117	124	131	137	144	151
648	158	164	171	178	184	191	198	204	211	218
649	224	231	238	245	251	258	265	271	278	285
650	291	298	305	311	318	325	331	338	345	351
N	L 0	1	2	3	4	5	6	7	8	9

P P

	8		7		6
1	0.8	1	0.7	1	0.6
2	1.6	2	1.4	2	1.2
3	2.4	3	2.1	3	1.8
4	3.2	4	2.8	4	2.4
5	4.0	5	3.5	5	3.0
6	4.8	6	4.2	6	3.6
7	5.6	7	4.9	7	4.2
8	6.4	8	5.6	8	4.8
9	7.2	9	6.3	9	5.4

N	L 0	1	2	3	4	5	6	7	8	9
650	81 291	298	305	311	318	325	331	338	345	351
651	358	365	371	378	385	391	398	405	411	418
652	425	431	438	445	451	458	465	471	478	485
653	491	498	505	511	518	525	531	538	544	551
654	558	564	571	578	584	591	598	604	611	617
655	624	631	637	644	651	657	664	671	677	684
656	690	697	704	710	717	723	730	737	743	750
657	757	763	770	776	783	790	796	803	809	816
658	823	829	836	842	849	856	862	869	875	882
659	889	895	902	908	915	921	928	935	941	948
660	954	961	968	974	981	987	994	*000	*007	*014
661	82 020	027	033	040	046	053	060	066	073	079
662	086	092	099	105	112	119	125	132	138	145
663	151	158	164	171	178	184	191	197	204	210
664	217	223	230	236	243	249	256	263	269	276
665	282	289	295	302	308	315	321	328	334	341
666	347	354	360	367	373	380	387	393	400	406
667	413·	419	426	432	439	445	452	458	465	471
668	478	484	491	497	504	510	517	523	530	536
669	543	549	556	562	569	575	582	588	595	601
670	607	614	620	627	633	640	646	653	659	666
671	672	679	685	692	698	705	711	718	724	730
672	737	743	750	756	763	769	776	782	789	795
673	802	808	814	821	827	834	840	847	853	860
674	866	872	879	885	892	898	905	911	918	924
675	930	937	943	950	956	963	969	975	982	988
676	995	*001	*008	*014	*020	*027	*033	*040	*046	*052
677	83 059	065	072	078	085	091	097	104	110	117
678	123	129	136	142	149	155	161	168	174	181
679	187	193	200	206	213	219	225	232	238	245
680	251	257	264	270	276	283	289	296	302	308
681	315	321	327	334	340	347	353	359	366	372
682	378	385	391	398	404	410	417	423	429	436
683	442	448	455	461	467	474	480	487	493	499
684	506	512	518	525	531	537	544	550	556	563
685	569	575	582	588	594	601	607	613	620	626
686	632	639	645	651	658	664	670	677	683	689
687	696	702	708	715	721	727	734	740	746	753
688	759	765	771	778	784	790	797	803	809	816
689	822	828	835	841	847	853	860	866	872	879
690	885	891	897	904	910	916	923	929	935	942
691	948	954	960	967	973	979	985	992	998	*004
692	84 011	017	023	029	036	042	048	055	061	067
693	073	080	086	092	098	105	111	117	123	130
694	136	142	148	155	161	167	173	180	186	192
695	198	205	211	217	223	230	236	242	248	255
696	261	267	273	280	286	292	298	305	311	317
697	323	330	336	342	348	354	361	367	373	379
698	386	392	398	404	410	417	423	429	435	442
699	448	454	460	466	473	479	485	491	497	504
700	510	516	522	528	535	541	547	553	559	566
N	L 0	1	2	3	4	5	6	7	8	9

P P

7

1	0.7
2	1.4
3	2.1
4	2.8
5	3.5
6	4.2
7	4.9
8	5.6
9	6.3

6

1	0.6
2	1.2
3	1.8
4	2.4
5	3.0
6	3.6
7	4.2
8	4.8
9	5.4

700—750

N	L 0	1	2	3	4	5	6	7	8	9
700	84 510	516	522	528	535	541	547	553	559	566
701	572	578	584	590	597	603	609	615	621	628
702	634	640	646	652	658	665	671	677	683	689
703	696	702	708	714	720	726	733	739	745	751
704	757	763	770	776	782	788	794	800	807	813
705	819	825	831	837	844	850	856	862	868	874
706	880	887	893	899	905	911	917	924	930	936
707	942	948	954	960	967	973	979	985	991	997
708	85 003	009	016	022	028	034	040	046	052	058
709	065	071	077	083	089	095	101	107	114	120
710	126	132	138	144	150	156	163	169	175	181
711	187	193	199	205	211	217	224	230	236	242
712	248	254	260	266	272	278	285	291	297	303
713	309	315	321	327	333	339	345	352	358	364
714	370	376	382	388	394	400	406	412	418	425
715	431	437	443	449	455	461	467	473	479	485
716	491	497	503	509	516	522	528	534	540	546
717	552	558	564	570	576	582	588	594	600	606
718	612	618	625	631	637	643	649	655	661	667
719	673	679	685	691	697	703	709	715	721	727
720	733	739	745	751	757	763	769	775	781	788
721	794	800	806	812	818	824	830	836	842	848
722	854	860	866	872	878	884	890	896	902	908
723	914	920	926	932	938	944	950	956	962	968
724	974	980	986	992	998	*004	*010	*016	*022	*028
725	86 034	040	046	052	058	064	070	076	082	088
726	094	100	106	112	118	124	130	136	141	147
727	153	159	165	171	177	183	189	195	201	207
728	213	219	225	231	237	243	249	255	261	267
729	273	279	285	291	297	303	308	314	320	326
730	332	338	344	350	356	362	368	374	380	386
731	392	398	404	410	415	421	427	433	439	445
732	451	457	463	469	475	481	487	493	499	504
733	510	516	522	528	534	540	546	552	558	564
734	570	576	581	587	593	599	605	611	617	623
735	629	635	641	646	652	658	664	670	676	682
736	688	694	700	705	711	717	723	729	735	741
737	747	753	759	764	770	776	782	788	794	800
738	806	812	817	823	829	835	841	847	853	859
739	864	870	876	882	888	894	900	906	911	917
740	923	929	935	941	947	953	958	964	970	976
741	982	988	994	999	*005	*011	*017	*023	*029	*035
742	87 040	046	052	058	064	070	075	081	087	093
743	099	105	111	116	122	128	134	140	146	151
744	157	163	169	175	181	186	192	198	204	210
745	216	221	227	233	239	245	251	256	262	268
746	274	280	286	291	297	303	309	315	320	326
747	332	338	344	349	355	361	367	373	379	384
748	390	396	402	408	413	419	425	431	437	442
749	448	454	460	466	471	477	483	489	495	500
750	506	512	518	523	529	535	541	547	552	558
N	L 0	1	2	3	4	5	6	7	8	9

P P

7
1	0.7
2	1.4
3	2.1
4	2.8
5	3.5
6	4.2
7	4.9
8	5.6
9	6.3

6
1	0.6
2	1.2
3	1.8
4	2.4
5	3.0
6	3.6
7	4.2
8	4.8
9	5.4

5
1	0.5
2	1.0
3	1.5
4	2.0
5	2.5
6	3.0
7	3.5
8	4.0
9	4.5

750—800

N	L 0	1	2	3	4	5	6	7	8	9
750	87 506	512	518	523	529	535	541	547	552	558
751	564	570	576	581	587	593	599	604	610	616
752	622	628	633	639	645	651	656	662	668	674
753	679	685	691	697	703	708	714	720	726	731
754	737	743	749	754	760	766	772	777	783	789
755	795	800	806	812	818	823	829	835	841	846
756	852	858	864	869	875	881	887	892	898	904
757	910	915	921	927	933	938	944	950	955	961
758	967	973	978	984	990	996	*001	*007	*013	*018
759	88 024	030	036	041	047	053	058	064	070	076
760	081	087	093	098	104	110	116	121	127	133
761	138	144	150	156	161	167	173	178	184	190
762	195	201	207	213	218	224	230	235	241	247
763	252	258	264	270	275	281	287	292	298	304
764	309	315	321	326	332	338	343	349	355	360
765	366	372	377	383	389	395	400	406	412	417
766	423	429	434	440	446	451	457	463	468	474
767	480	485	491	497	502	508	513	519	525	530
768	536	542	547	553	559	564	570	576	581	587
769	593	598	604	610	615	621	627	632	638	643
770	649	655	660	666	672	677	683	689	694	700
771	705	711	717	722	728	734	739	745	750	756
772	762	767	773	779	784	790	795	801	807	812
773	818	824	829	835	840	846	852	857	863	868
774	874	880	885	891	897	902	908	913	919	925
775	930	936	941	947	953	958	964	969	975	981
776	986	992	997	*003	*009	*014	*020	*025	*031	*037
777	89 042	048	053	059	064	070	076	081	087	092
778	098	104	109	115	120	126	131	137	143	148
779	154	159	165	170	176	182	187	193	198	204
780	209	215	221	226	232	237	243	248	254	260
781	265	271	276	282	287	293	298	304	310	315
782	321	326	332	337	343	348	354	360	365	371
783	376	382	387	393	398	404	409	415	421	426
784	432	437	443	448	454	459	465	470	476	481
785	487	492	498	504	509	515	520	526	531	537
786	542	548	553	559	564	570	575	581	586	592
787	597	603	609	614	620	625	631	636	642	647
788	653	658	664	669	675	680	686	691	697	702
789	708	713	719	724	730	735	741	746	752	757
790	763	768	774	779	785	790	796	801	807	812
791	818	823	829	834	840	845	851	856	862	867
792	873	878	883	889	894	900	905	911	916	922
793	927	933	938	944	949	955	960	966	971	977
794	982	988	993	998	*004	*009	*015	*020	*026	*031
795	90 037	042	048	053	059	064	069	075	080	086
796	091	097	102	108	113	119	124	129	135	140
797	146	151	157	162	168	173	179	184	189	195
798	200	206	211	217	222	227	233	238	244	249
799	255	260	266	271	276	282	287	293	298	304
800	309	314	320	325	331	336	342	347	352	358
N	L 0	1	2	3	4	5	6	7	8	9

P P

6	
1	0.6
2	1.2
3	1.8
4	2.4
5	3.0
6	3.6
7	4.2
8	4.8
9	5.4

5	
1	0.5
2	1.0
3	1.5
4	2.0
5	2.5
6	3.0
7	3.5
8	4.0
9	4.5

800—850

N	L 0	1	2	3	4	5	6	7	8	9	P P	
800	90 309	314	320	325	331	336	342	347	352	358		
801	363	369	374	380	385	390	396	401	407	412		
802	417	423	428	434	439	445	450	455	461	466		
803	472	477	482	488	493	499	504	509	515	520		
804	526	531	536	542	547	553	558	563	569	574		
805	580	585	590	596	601	607	612	617	623	628		
806	634	639	644	650	655	660	666	671	677	682		
807	687	693	698	703	709	714	720	725	730	736		
808	741	747	752	757	763	768	773	779	784	789		
809	795	800	806	811	816	822	827	832	838	843		
810	849	854	859	865	870	875	881	886	891	897		
811	902	907	913	918	924	929	934	940	945	950		6
812	956	961	966	972	977	982	988	993	998	*004		
813	91 009	014	020	025	030	036	041	046	052	057	1	0.6
814	062	068	073	078	084	089	094	100	105	110	2	1.2
815	116	121	126	132	137	142	148	153	158	164	3	1.8
816	169	174	180	185	190	196	201	206	212	217	4	2.4
817	222	228	233	238	243	249	254	259	265	270	5	3.0
818	275	281	286	291	297	302	307	312	318	323	6	3.6
819	328	334	339	344	350	355	360	365	371	376	7	4.2
820	381	387	392	397	403	408	413	418	424	429	8	4.8
821	434	440	445	450	455	461	466	471	477	482	9	5.4
822	487	492	498	503	508	514	519	524	529	535		
823	540	545	551	556	561	566	572	577	582	587		
824	593	598	603	609	614	619	624	630	635	640		
825	645	651	656	661	666	672	677	682	687	693		
826	698	703	709	714	719	724	730	735	740	745		
827	751	756	761	766	772	777	782	787	793	798		
828	803	808	814	819	824	829	834	840	845	850		
829	855	861	866	871	876	882	887	892	897	903		
830	908	913	918	924	929	934	939	944	950	955		
831	960	965	971	976	981	986	991	997	*002	*007		5
832	92 012	018	023	028	033	038	044	049	054	059	1	0.5
833	065	070	075	080	085	091	096	101	106	111	2	1.0
834	117	122	127	132	137	143	148	153	158	163	3	1.5
835	169	174	179	184	189	195	200	205	210	215	4	2.0
836	221	226	231	236	241	247	252	257	262	267	5	2.5
837	273	278	283	288	293	298	304	309	314	319	6	3.0
838	324	330	335	340	345	350	355	361	366	371	7	3.5
839	376	381	387	392	397	402	407	412	418	423	8	4.0
840	428	433	438	443	449	454	459	464	469	474	9	4.5
841	480	485	490	495	500	505	511	516	521	526		
842	531	536	542	547	552	557	562	567	572	578		
843	583	588	593	598	603	609	614	619	624	629		
844	634	639	645	650	655	660	665	670	675	681		
845	686	691	696	701	706	711	716	722	727	732		
846	737	742	747	752	758	763	768	773	778	783		
847	788	793	799	804	809	814	819	824	829	834		
848	840	845	850	855	860	865	870	875	881	886		
849	891	896	901	906	911	916	921	927	932	937		
850	942	947	952	957	962	967	973	978	983	988		
N	L 0	1	2	3	4	5	6	7	8	9	P P	

850—900

N	L 0	1	2	3	4	5	6	7	8	9
850	92 942	947	952	957	962	967	973	978	983	988
851	993	998	*003	*008	*013	*018	*024	*029	*034	*039
852	93 044	049	054	059	064	069	075	080	085	090
853	095	100	105	110	115	120	125	131	136	141
854	146	151	156	161	166	171	176	181	186	192
855	197	202	207	212	217	222	227	232	237	242
856	247	252	258	263	268	273	278	283	288	293
857	298	303	308	313	318	323	328	334	339	344
858	349	354	359	364	369	374	379	384	389	394
859	399	404	409	414	420	425	430	435	440	445
860	450	455	460	465	470	475	480	485	490	495
861	500	505	510	515	520	526	531	536	541	546
862	551	556	561	566	571	576	581	586	591	596
863	601	606	611	616	621	626	631	636	641	646
864	651	656	661	666	671	676	682	687	692	697
865	702	707	712	717	722	727	732	737	742	747
866	752	757	762	767	772	777	782	787	792	797
867	802	807	812	817	822	827	832	837	842	847
868	852	857	862	867	872	877	882	887	892	897
869	902	907	912	917	922	927	932	937	942	947
870	952	957	962	967	972	977	982	987	992	997
871	94 002	007	012	017	022	027	032	037	042	047
872	052	057	062	067	072	077	082	086	091	096
873	101	106	111	116	121	126	131	136	141	146
874	151	156	161	166	171	176	181	186	191	196
875	201	206	211	216	221	226	231	236	240	245
876	250	255	260	265	270	275	280	285	290	295
877	300	305	310	315	320	325	330	335	340	345
878	349	354	359	364	369	374	379	384	389	394
879	399	404	409	414	419	424	429	433	438	443
880	448	453	458	463	468	473	478	483	488	493
881	498	503	507	512	517	522	527	532	537	542
882	547	552	557	562	567	571	576	581	586	591
883	596	601	606	611	616	621	626	630	635	640
884	645	650	655	660	665	670	675	680	685	689
885	694	699	704	709	714	719	724	729	734	738
886	743	748	753	758	763	768	773	778	783	787
887	792	797	802	807	812	817	822	827	832	836
888	841	846	851	856	861	866	871	876	880	885
889	890	895	900	905	910	915	919	924	929	934
890	939	944	949	954	959	963	968	973	978	983
891	988	993	998	*002	*007	*012	*017	*022	*027	*032
892	95 036	041	046	051	056	061	066	071	075	080
893	085	090	095	100	105	109	114	119	124	129
894	134	139	143	148	153	158	163	168	173	177
895	182	187	192	197	202	207	211	216	221	226
896	231	236	240	245	250	255	260	265	270	274
897	279	284	289	294	299	303	308	313	318	323
898	328	332	337	342	347	352	357	361	366	371
899	376	381	386	390	395	400	405	410	415	419
900	424	429	434	439	444	448	453	458	463	468

P P

	6
1	0.6
2	1.2
3	1.8
4	2.4
5	3.0
6	3.6
7	4.2
8	4.8
9	5.4

	5
1	0.5
2	1.0
3	1.5
4	2.0
5	2.5
6	3.0
7	3.5
8	4.0
9	4.5

	4
1	0.4
2	0.8
3	1.2
4	1.6
5	2.0
6	2.4
7	2.8
8	3.2
9	3.6

N	L 0	1	2	3	4	5	6	7	8	9	P P

APPENDIX IV
900—950

N	L 0	1	2	3	4	5	6	7	8	9		P P
900	95 424	429	434	439	444	448	453	458	463	468		
901	472	477	482	487	492	497	501	506	511	516		
902	521	525	530	535	540	545	550	554	559	564		—
903	569	574	578	583	588	593	598	602	607	612		
904	617	622	626	631	636	641	646	650	655	660		
905	665	670	674	679	684	689	694	698	703	708		
906	713	718	722	727	732	737	742	746	751	756		
907	761	766	770	775	780	785	789	794	799	804		
908	809	813	818	823	828	832	837	842	847	852		
909	856	861	866	871	875	880	885	890	895	899		
910	904	909	914	918	923	928	933	938	942	947		
911	952	957	961	966	971	976	980	985	990	995		
912	999	*004	*009	*014	*019	*023	*028	*033	*038	*042		**5**
913	96 047	052	057	061	066	071	076	080	085	090		1 | 0.5
914	095	099	104	109	114	118	123	128	133	137		2 | 1.0
915	142	147	152	156	161	166	171	175	180	185		3 | 1.5
916	190	194	199	204	209	213	218	223	227	232		4 | 2.0
917	237	242	246	251	256	261	265	270	275	280		5 | 2.5
918	284	289	294	298	303	308	313	317	322	327		6 | 3.0
919	332	336	341	346	350	355	360	365	369	374		7 | 3.5
920	379	384	388	393	398	402	407	412	417	421		8 | 4.0
921	426	431	435	440	445	450	454	459	464	468		9 | 4.5
922	473	478	483	487	492	497	501	506	511	515		
923	520	525	530	534	539	544	548	553	558	562		
924	567	572	577	581	586	591	595	600	605	609		
925	614	619	624	628	633	638	642	647	652	656		
926	661	666	670	675	680	685	689	694	699	703		
927	708	713	717	722	727	731	736	741	745	750		
928	755	759	764	769	774	778	783	788	792	797		
929	802	806	811	816	820	825	830	834	839	844		
930	848	853	858	862	867	872	876	881	886	890		
931	895	900	904	909	914	918	923	928	932	937		**4**
932	942	946	951	956	960	965	970	974	979	984		1 | 0.4
933	988	993	997	*002	*007	*011	*016	*021	*025	*030		2 | 0.8
934	97 035	039	044	049	053	058	063	067	072	077		3 | 1.2
935	081	086	090	095	100	104	109	114	118	123		4 | 1.6
936	128	132	137	142	146	151	155	160	165	169		5 | 2.0
937	174	179	183	188	192	197	202	206	211	216		6 | 2.4
938	220	225	230	234	239	243	248	253	257	262		7 | 2.8
939	267	271	276	280	285	290	294	299	304	308		8 | 3.2
940	313	317	322	327	331	336	340	345	350	354		9 | 3.6
941	359	364	368	373	377	382	387	391	396	400		
942	405	410	414	419	424	428	433	437	442	447		
943	451	456	460	465	470	474	479	483	488	493		
944	497	502	506	511	516	520	525	529	534	539		
945	543	548	552	557	562	566	571	575	580	585		
946	589	594	598	603	607	612	617	621	626	630		
947	635	640	644	649	653	658	663	667	672	676		
	681	685	690	695	699	704	708	713	717	722		
		731	736	740	745	749	754	759	763	768		
		782	786	791	795	800	804	809	813			
			3	4	5	6	7	8	9			P P